HOW TO GET YOUR TRIVIA ON!

Pull on your flairs, brush off your studded leather jacket, bust out the corduroy, and get ready for a ton of fun with the *70s Trivia Quiz!* This book contains 601 questions over 85 rounds and is divided into 4 categories:

MOVIES......1   TV SHOWS   53   MUSIC......105   GAMES & TECH......157

Each round contains questions on one side of the page with the answers printed on the reverse side. This means that the person reading the questions can also participate in the game without seeing the answers.

If playing in a group, divide into teams, or play as individuals, and nominate a host to read out the questions. You can even rotate the host each round. Choose how many rounds you want to play in total and from what categories. Each team should number and write down their answers on a piece of paper. At the end of each round, ask the teams to swap and mark the answer sheets. The team with the highest score at the end of all rounds is the winner!

For playing solo, it is best to wait to the end of each round before checking answers and to write them on separate paper, so you don't accidentally see the answers to other questions.

Groovy—it's time to get your trivia on!

MOVIES

The 1970s provided A New Hope for studios and filmmakers, as the loosening of the Sting of restrictions on violence, language and adult content allowed them to open their Jaws for more gritty storylines and Close Encounter performances resulting in both critical acclaim and box office success for many of the decade's biggest films. The crime-drama genre dominated screens, while horror and westerns were also still widely popular.

Are you The Godfather of 70s movie trivia? Are you off to a Rocky start but ready to punch your way through this round? Then invite over some good (or even Bad) Company, and lock your Jaws into this Holy Grail of 70s movie questions. You've just got to ask yourself one question: "Do I feel lucky?"

Bond Films
QUESTIONS

1 How many different actors played the role of James Bond in movies during the 1970s?

2 Which Welsh singer performed the title song for *Diamonds Are Forever*?

3 Which actor played the character of Solitaire in *Live and Let Die*?

4 In the name of the fictional organization headed by criminal mastermind Ernst Stavro Blofeld, what do the initials in "SPECTRE" stand for?

5 Fill in the gaps below, one letter per gap, to complete the name of the title song from 1977's *The Spy Who Loved Me*:

_O_O_Y _O_S _T
_E_T_R

6 What is the full name of the antagonist who is nicknamed "The Man with the Golden Gun"?

7 What is the name of the steel-toothed assassin who appears in *The Spy Who Loved Me* and *Moonraker*?

Bond Films
ANSWERS

1 How many different actors played the role of James Bond in movies during the 1970s?

Two: Sean Connery and Roger Moore

Sean Connery reprised his role as an "official" James Bond for the final time in Diamonds Are Forever *(1971), after George Lazenby had taken over for one film in* On Her Majesty's Secret Service *(1969), although Connery later appeared in the "unofficial"* Never Say Never Again *(1983). After Roger Moore took the reins in 1973's* Live and Let Die, *he would go on to star in a further six films as the iconic spy, three of which were in the 1970s:* The Man with the Golden Gun, The Spy Who Loved Me *and* Moonraker.

2 Which Welsh singer performed the title song for *Diamonds Are Forever*?

Dame Shirley Bassey

3 Which actor played the character of Solitaire in *Live and Let Die*?

Jane Seymour

4 In the name of the fictional organization headed by criminal mastermind Ernst Stavro Blofeld, what do the initials in "SPECTRE" stand for?

Special Executive for Counterintelligence, Terrorism, Revenge and Extortion

5 Fill in the gaps below, one letter per gap, to complete the name of the title song from 1977's *The Spy Who Loved Me*:

_O_O_Y _O_S _T _E_T_R

Nobody Does It Better

6 What is the full name of the antagonist who is nicknamed "The Man with the Golden Gun"?

Francisco Scaramanga

7 What is the name of the steel-toothed assassin who appears in *The Spy Who Loved Me* and *Moonraker*?

Jaws

Comedies
QUESTIONS

1. What famous Irving Berlin song do Dr. Frankenstein, played by Gene Wilder, and The Monster, played by Peter Boyle, perform in *Young Frankenstein*, resulting in them being pelted with cabbages?

2. Steve Martin's first starring role in a feature film was as which character in the 1979 movie, *The Jerk*?

3. In which cult classic British comedy would you find the Knights Who Say "Ni!"?

4. Which 1972 comedy, based on a novel by Graham Greene, starred Maggie Smith as Aunt Augusta and Louis Gossett Jr. as Wordsworth?

5. In *The Pink Panther* series of movies, what nationality is Inspector Clouseau, later promoted to Chief Inspector?

6. Cleavon Little won the Best Newcomer BAFTA of 1975 for his role as Bart in which Mel Brooks black comedy Western?

7. What is Sonny Hooper's job, in the Burt Reynolds movie *Hooper* that acts as a tribute to that profession?

Comedies
ANSWERS

1 What famous Irving Berlin song do Dr. Frankenstein, played by Gene Wilder, and The Monster, played by Peter Boyle, perform in *Young Frankenstein*, resulting in them being pelted with cabbages?

Puttin' on the Ritz

Director Mel Brooks later said that it was the only fight he and Wilder had during the making of the film. Brooks felt the sequence was too silly and wouldn't work, Wilder convinced him to film it and see how it worked with test audiences. Brooks later said 'Of course, Gene was dead right because it took the movie to another level.'

2 Steve Martin's first starring role in a feature film was as which character in the 1979 movie, *The Jerk*?

Navin R. Johnson

3 In which cult classic British comedy would you find the Knights Who Say "Ni!"?

Monty Python and the Holy Grail

4 Which 1972 comedy, based on a novel by Graham Greene, starred Maggie Smith as Aunt Augusta and Louis Gossett Jr. as Wordsworth?

Travels With My Aunt

5 In *The Pink Panther* series of movies, what nationality is Inspector Clouseau, later promoted to Chief Inspector?

French

6 Cleavon Little won the Best Newcomer BAFTA of 1975 for his role as Bart in which Mel Brooks black comedy Western?

Blazing Saddles

7 What is Sonny Hooper's job, in the Burt Reynolds movie *Hooper* that acts as a tribute to that profession?

Stuntman

Action & Adventure
QUESTIONS

1 Which actress, whose big-screen debut was in 1971's *Beyond the Valley of the Dolls*, later went on to play Foxy Brown in the 1974 movie of the same name?

2 In which country does dystopian road movie *Mad Max* take place?

3 Which Bruce Lee film was released first: *The Way of the Dragon* or *Enter the Dragon*?

4 Unjumble the letters below to reveal the name of the actor who portrayed the titular role of John Shaft, in *Shaft*:

HORRID RUDE TRANCE (7, 9)

5 Which actor delivers the line, "Did he fire six shots, or only five? Well, to tell you the truth, in all this excitement, I've kinda lost track myself", in 1971's *Dirty Harry*?

6 Which 1970 comedy-drama heist film involves a crew of American GI's going AWOL in order to rob a French bank?

7 In 1977, which road movie had the tagline "What we have here is a total lack of respect for the law!"?

Action & Adventure
ANSWERS

1 Which actress, whose big-screen debut was in 1971's *Beyond the Valley of the Dolls*, later went on to play Foxy Brown in the 1974 movie of the same name?

Pam Grier

Grier became a staple of "Blaxploitation" films in the 1970s but later expanded her range of projects in the 1980s. In 1997 she went on to accept the lead role in Quentin Tarantino's major feature, Jackie Brown. Tarantino described her as "cinema's first female action star".

2 In which country does dystopian road movie *Mad Max* take place?

Australia

3 Which Bruce Lee film was released first: *The Way of the Dragon* or *Enter the Dragon*?

The Way of the Dragon was made in 1972, with Enter the Dragon, Bruce Lee's final film, following in 1973.

4 Unjumble the letters below to reveal the name of the actor who portrayed the titular role of John Shaft, in *Shaft*:

HORRID RUDE TRANCE (7, 9)

Richard Roundtree

5 Which actor delivers the line, "Did he fire six shots, or only five? Well, to tell you the truth, in all this excitement, I've kinda lost track myself", in 1971's *Dirty Harry*?

Clint Eastwood

6 Which 1970 comedy-drama heist film involves a crew of American GIs going AWOL in order to rob a French bank?

Kelly's Heroes

7 In 1977, which road movie had the tagline "What we have here is a total lack of respect for the law!"?

Smokey and the Bandit

Award Winners 1
QUESTIONS

1 Who was nominated for both Best Director and Best Actor at the 1977 Oscars, but ended up winning only one of the two awards?

2 For which film did future UK Member of Parliament, Glenda Jackson, win Best Actress at the Academy Awards held in 1970?

3 Which Motown singer won the 1973 Golden Globe for Most Promising Newcomer in her role as Billie Holiday in *Lady Sings the Blues*?

4 Which Oscar-winning film had the tagline, "His whole life was a million-to-one shot"?

5 What character is the antagonist to Jack Nicholson's Randle McMurphy, in *One Flew Over the Cuckoo's Nest*?

6 Which actor did not collect his own Oscar in 1973 but sent civil-rights activist Sacheen Littlefeather to do so instead, in a protest against Hollywood's portrayal of Native Americans?

7 Restore the missing vowels to reveal the musician who was awarded the Academy Award in 1972 for Best Original Song, for *Theme from Shaft*:

SC   HYS

Award Winners 1
ANSWERS

1 Who was nominated for both Best Director and Best Actor at the 1977 Oscars, but ended up winning only one of the two awards?

Woody Allen

Allen was nominated for both directing and acting in Annie Hall. The film won three of its overall four nominations, which also included Best Actress (for Diane Keaton) and Best Screenplay, but Allen lost out on Best Actor to Richard Dreyfuss's appearance in The Goodbye Girl. At only 93 minutes, Annie Hall remains one of the shortest films ever to win Best Picture.

2 For which film did future UK Member of Parliament, Glenda Jackson, win Best Actress at the Academy Awards held in 1970?

Women in Love

3 Which Motown singer won the 1973 Golden Globe for Most Promising Newcomer in her role as Billie Holiday in *Lady Sings the Blues*?

Diana Ross

4 Which Oscar-winning film had the tagline, "His whole life was a million-to-one shot"?

Rocky

5 What character is the antagonist to Jack Nicholson's Randle McMurphy, in *One Flew Over the Cuckoo's Nest*?

Nurse Ratched

6 Which actor did not collect his own Oscar in 1973 but sent civil-rights activist Sacheen Littlefeather to do so instead, in a protest against Hollywood's portrayal of Native Americans?

Marlon Brando

7 Restore the missing vowels to reveal the musician who was awarded the Academy Award in 1972 for Best Original Song, for *Theme from Shaft*:

SC   HYS

Isaac Hayes

Out of This World 1
QUESTIONS

1 What method do the humans and aliens use to communicate when they meet in *Close Encounters of the Third Kind*?

2 Who was the last survivor of the Nostromo, the doomed ship in 1979's *Alien*?

3 In the 1978 film, *Superman*, who played Jor-El, Superman's father?

4 Can you name the actress who played the role of Lois Lane in the 1978 *Superman* movie?

5 Which TV science fiction show made the transition to the big screen with its first motion picture in 1979, bearing the subtitle "The Motion Picture"?

6 What is the title of the 1970 sequel to the 1968 *Planet of the Apes*?

7 Complete the famous tagline from *Alien*:

"In space no one can hear you _____".

1 What method do the humans and aliens use to communicate when they meet in *Close Encounters of the Third Kind*?

Musical notes

The exchange takes place when the Mothership lands at Devil's Tower, Wyoming. Ever since the release of the movie, there has been a nightly screening at the adjacent Devil's Tower/ Black Hills KOA Campground, making it by some estimates one of the most-screened movies in the world.

2 Who was the last survivor of the Nostromo, the doomed ship in 1979's *Alien*?

Ripley, played by Sigourney Weaver

3 In the 1978 film, *Superman*, who played Jor-El, Superman's father?

Marlon Brando

4 Can you name the actress who played the role of Lois Lane in the 1978 *Superman* movie?

Margot Kidder

5 Which TV science fiction show made the transition to the big screen with its first motion picture in 1979, bearing the subtitle "The Motion Picture"?

Star Trek

6 What is the title of the 1970 sequel to the 1968 *Planet of the Apes*?

Beneath the Planet of the Apes

7 Complete the famous tagline from *Alien*:

"In space no one can hear you _____."

Scream

Musicals
QUESTIONS

1 What is the name of the school attended by both Danny and Sandy in *Grease*?

2 According to *The Rocky Horror Picture Show*, during the "Time Warp", what must you do after a jump to the left?

3 Rearrange the fragments on the line below to reveal the name of the alien race that features in the *The Rocky Horror Picture Show*:

The NS AN AN IA LV SY TR

4 Which stage musical was turned into a then-controversial 1973 film which stars Ted Neeley in the title role?

5 Which writer, choreographer, and theatrical director went on to direct the film version of *Cabaret*?

6 What was unusual about the shootout at the end of *Bugsy Malone*?

7 The cast of which 1978 musical includes Diana Ross, Michael Jackson, and Richard Pryor?

1 What is the name of the school attended by both Danny and Sandy in *Grease*?

Rydell High

The exterior location for the movie was in reality Venice High School in Los Angeles, which has an impressive list of famous alumni that includes actor Beau Bridges, land-speed record holder Craig Breedlove, and the first female pilot to fly solo across the Pacific, Betty Miller.

2 According to *The Rocky Horror Picture Show*, during the "Time Warp", what must you do after a jump to the left?

Take a step to the right

3 Rearrange the fragments on the line below to reveal the name of the alien race that features in the *The Rocky Horror Picture Show*:

The NS AN AN IA LV SY TR

The Transylvanians

4 Which stage musical was turned into a then-controversial 1973 film which stars Ted Neeley in the title role?

Jesus Christ Superstar

5 Which writer, choreographer, and theatrical director went on to direct the film version of *Cabaret*?

Bob Fosse

6 What was unusual about the shootout at the end of *Bugsy Malone*?

It was a cream pie fight/ splurge gun fight

7 The cast of which 1978 musical includes Diana Ross, Michael Jackson, and Richard Pryor?

The Wiz

Actors at the Oscars
QUESTIONS

1. Which actor refused to accept the Best Actor Oscar he had been awarded for *Patton*, at the 1971 Academy Awards?

2. The year 1975 saw three actors from the same movie nominated for Best Supporting Actor at the Oscars. What was that movie?

3. He won one of them, but how many times was Jack Nicholson nominated for an Academy Award during the period from 1970 to 1979 inclusive?

4. Which Marx brother accepted an honorary Oscar at the ceremony in 1974?

5. Chief Dan George was nominated for Best Supporting Actor in 1971 for which Dustin Hoffman movie?

6. Unscramble the letters to reveal which legendary screen actor received a 12-minute standing ovation on receipt of their honorary Oscar in 1972:

   RICH PACE IN HALL (7, 7)

7. Which famous actor, writer, producer, and director, widely considered one of the most legendary filmmakers of all time, was awarded an honorary Oscar in 1971?

Actors at the Oscars
ANSWERS

1 Which actor refused to accept the Best Actor Oscar he had been awarded for *Patton*, at the 1971 Academy Awards?

George C. Scott

Scott didn't show up to the ceremony after telling the Academy that he disagreed with the notion of pitting actors against one another. The producer of Patton, Frank McCarthy, accepted the award on Scott's behalf, but returned it the next day in accordance with the actor's request.

2 The year 1975 saw three actors from the same movie nominated for Best Supporting Actor at the Oscars. What was that movie?

The Godfather Part II

3 He won one of them, but how many times was Jack Nicholson nominated for an Academy Award during the period from 1970 to 1979 inclusive?

Five times

4 Which Marx brother accepted an honorary Oscar at the ceremony in 1974?

Groucho

5 Chief Dan George was nominated for Best Supporting Actor in 1971 for which Dustin Hoffman movie?

Little Big Man

6 Unscramble the letters to reveal which legendary screen actor received a 12-minute standing ovation on receipt of their honorary Oscar in 1972:

RICH PACE IN HALL (7, 7)

Charlie Chaplin

7 Which famous actor, writer, producer, and director, widely considered one of the most legendary filmmakers of all time, was awarded an honorary Oscar in 1971?

Orson Welles

Jaws vs King Kong
QUESTIONS

1 Was Jaws or King Kong more successful? Specifically, which movie, out of *Jaws*, *Jaws 2*, and the 1976 *King Kong*, made the most money at the worldwide box office?

2 Which film, *Jaws* or *King Kong*, doesn't show the monster until 53 minutes into its running time?

3 Was it the shark animatronic in the *Jaws* movies, or the ape animatronic from *King Kong*, that was nicknamed Bruce in homage to the director's lawyer?

4 Which animal, Jaws or King Kong, was created using a 6.5-ton animatronic model?

5 Out of *Jaws*, *Jaws 2*, and *King Kong*, which movie contains the most character deaths?

6 Which film attracted 30,000 unpaid extras for a key scene, leading to an army of people so large that it alarmed the local Port Authority and led to the filming being canceled? It was later filmed with a safer number of people.

7 "You don't have to worry about being sued, or being ruined if this turns out to be what I think it is, because there won't be anybody here!" is a line which appears in which movie: *Jaws*, *Jaws 2*, or *King Kong*?

Jaws vs King Kong
ANSWERS

1 Was Jaws or King Kong more successful? Specifically, which movie, out of *Jaws*, *Jaws 2*, and the 1976 *King Kong*, made the most money at the worldwide box office?

Jaws

> *The movie pulled in $472 million from a $9 million budget. Jaws 2 made $208 million, while King Kong made $90.6 million. Jaws is credited with the birth of the "summer blockbuster" concept—a hyped-up, large-scale, potentially highly profitable "event" movie made to tempt audiences into a darkened cinema during the height of the summer season.*

2 Which film, *Jaws* or *King Kong*, doesn't show the monster until 53 minutes into its running time?

King Kong

3 Was it the shark animatronic in the *Jaws* movies, or the ape animatronic from *King Kong*, that was nicknamed Bruce in homage to the director's lawyer?

The shark animatronic from Jaws

4 Which animal, Jaws or King Kong, was created using a 6.5-ton animatronic model?

King Kong

5 Out of *Jaws*, *Jaws 2*, and *King Kong*, which movie contains the most character deaths?

King Kong

6 Which film attracted 30,000 unpaid extras for a key scene, leading to an army of people so large that it alarmed the local Port Authority and led to the filming being canceled? It was later filmed with a safer number of people.

King Kong

7 "You don't have to worry about being sued, or being ruined if this turns out to be what I think it is, because there won't be anybody here!" is a line which appears in which movie: *Jaws*, *Jaws 2*, or *King Kong*?

Jaws 2

Star Wars 1
QUESTIONS

1 A recording of which animal forms the core basis of the sound made by the TIE fighters, in *Star Wars*?

2 In *Star Wars*, what was the name of the deadly battle station governed by Grand Moff Tarkin?

3 Which actress, the daughter of actress Debbie Reynolds, played the role of Princess Leia?

4 What are the first names of Luke Skywalker's aunt and uncle?

5 According to Princess Leia's message, which wars did Obi-Wan Kenobi help her father in?

6 Complete this Obi-Wan Kenobi quote:

"Mos Eisley Spaceport. You will never find a more wretched hive of scum and _____".

7 Han Solo owes money to which gangster, not seen on screen in the original release of *Star Wars* but later added digitally to subsequent re-releases?

Star Wars 1

ANSWERS

1 A recording of which animal forms the core basis of the sound made by the TIE fighters, in *Star Wars*?

An elephant

Sound designer Ben Burtt combined the sounds of an elephant's "scream" with that of tires on a wet road to create the iconic sound of the TIE Fighters. The lightsaber sounds, meanwhile, were made by combining the sound of a 35mm projector with the hum of a 1970s-era tube television screen.

2 In *Star Wars*, what was the name of the deadly battle station governed by Grand Moff Tarkin?

The Death Star

3 Which actress, the daughter of actress Debbie Reynolds, played the role of Princess Leia?

Carrie Fisher

4 What are the first names of Luke Skywalker's aunt and uncle?

Aunt Beru and Uncle Owen

5 According to Princess Leia's message, which wars did Obi-Wan Kenobi help her father in?

The Clone Wars

6 Complete this Obi-Wan Kenobi quote:

"Mos Eisley Spaceport. You will never find a more wretched hive of scum and _____ ".

Villainy

7 Han Solo owes money to which gangster, not seen on screen in the original release of *Star Wars* but later added digitally to subsequent re-releases?

Jabba (the Hutt)

Romance
QUESTIONS

1. Barbra Streisand sang the title song for which 1973 movie, in which she also played a starring role?

2. Originally based on Dustin Hoffman's experiences as a struggling actor, what is the title of the 1977 romantic hit movie that stars Marsha Mason as Paula and Richard Dreyfuss as Elliot?

3. Which offbeat 1971 romance was selected for preservation in the National Film Registry in 1997, and features a love affair with a 60-year age gap between the protagonists?

4. Which F. Scott Fitzgerald novel was adapted into a 1974 movie starring both Robert Redford and Mia Farrow?

5. Unjumble the following letters in order to spell out the name of the writer of *The Goodbye Girl*:

   SMILE ON IN (4, 5)

6. "I don't want to live in a city where the only cultural advantage is that you can make a right turn on a red light" is a quote from which romantic movie?

7. Restore the missing vowels to reveal the actress who plays Jennifer "Jenny" Cavilleri in the movie *Love Story*:

   L MCGRW

Romance
ANSWERS

1 Barbra Streisand sang the title song for which 1973 movie, in which she also played a starring role?

The Way We Were

On hearing the song for the first time, Streisand made two suggestions on how to improve it. First, a shift in melody to help make it "soar" at a crucial point, and secondly that the opening line be changed from "Daydreams light the corner of my mind" to "Memories light the corner of my mind".

2 Originally based on Dustin Hoffman's experiences as a struggling actor, what is the title of the 1977 romantic hit movie that stars Marsha Mason as Paula and Richard Dreyfuss as Elliot?

The Goodbye Girl

3 Which offbeat 1971 romance was selected for preservation in the National Film Registry in 1997, and features a love affair with a 60-year age gap between the protagonists?

Harold and Maude

4 Which F. Scott Fitzgerald novel was adapted into a 1974 movie starring both Robert Redford and Mia Farrow?

The Great Gatsby

5 Unjumble the following letters in order to spell out the name of the writer of *The Goodbye Girl*:

SMILE ON IN (4, 5)

Neil Simon

6 "I don't want to live in a city where the only cultural advantage is that you can make a right turn on a red light" is a quote from which romantic movie?

Annie Hall

7 Restore the missing vowels to reveal the actress who plays Jennifer "Jenny" Cavilleri in the movie *Love Story*:

L MCGRW

Ali MacGraw

Horror
QUESTIONS

1. Which Oscar-winning film created mass hysteria among cinema goers when it was first released in 1973?

2. Who played the role of Laurie Strode in 1978's *Halloween*?

3. In *The Omen*, what is Damien's adoptive surname?

4. Which 1976 movie tells the story of a shy girl unleashing her telekinetic powers on her school, having been humiliated at her senior prom?

5. What religion does the lead character of Sergeant Howie follow in 1973's *The Wicker Man*?

6. What is the name of the cat in *Alien*, kept aboard the USCSS Nostromo as Ripley's pet?

7. In which US state does the titular "massacre" take place, in Tobe Hooper's 1974 horror movie?

1 Which Oscar-winning film created mass hysteria among cinema goers when it was first released in 1973?

The Exorcist

> *There was enormous hype around the movie, fueled by stories about it being a "cursed production" and the apparent use of subliminal imagery within the film itself. On its release there were reports of mass panic, and of people fainting or unable to make it through the entire film. At some screenings, the Catholic Church were said to be on hand to counsel people who were affected by it.*

2 Who played the role of Laurie Strode in 1978's *Halloween*?

Jamie Lee Curtis

3 In *The Omen*, what is Damien's adoptive surname?

Thorn

4 Which 1976 movie tells the story of a shy girl unleashing her telekinetic powers on her school, having been humiliated at her senior prom?

Carrie

5 What religion does the lead character of Sergeant Howie follow in 1973's *The Wicker Man*?

Christianity

6 What is the name of the cat in *Alien*, kept aboard the USCSS Nostromo as Ripley's pet?

Jonesy / Jones

7 In which US state does the titular "massacre" take place, in Tobe Hooper's 1974 horror movie?

Texas—in *The Texas Chainsaw Massacre*

Pot Luck 1
QUESTIONS

1 Which former weightlifter appeared in a major role in *Star Wars*, as well as a more minor role in *A Clockwork Orange*?

2 Which writer/director went on holiday to Hawaii with Steven Spielberg rather than attend the premiere of his own 1977 movie, so convinced was he that it would be a failure?

3 "Sunrise, Sunset" is a song that can be found in which 1971 musical?

4 Restore the missing vowels and change the spacing to reveal the title of a gritty movie, telling the story of a Michael Caine character returning to his roots in Newcastle upon Tyne:

G TCR TR

5 Which Stanley Kubrick film famously utilized a special technique for filming in candlelight, to avoid the need for traditional film lighting?

6 Which actress played the role of Carrie in the film of the same name?

7 What is the name of the actor who played the world champion, Apollo, in *Rocky*?

Pot Luck 1
ANSWERS

1 Which former weightlifter appeared in a major role in *Star Wars*, as well as a more minor role in *A Clockwork Orange*?

David Prowse

Prowse wore the Darth Vader suit in Star Wars, *while in A Clockwork Orange he played Julian, a manservant. An actor and body builder, Prowse was reportedly upset that his Bristolian accent was re-dubbed by James Earl Jones for Star Wars. He was also well-known in the UK for his role as the "Green Cross Code" man in a series of commercials that teach children about crossing the road safely.*

2 Which writer/director went on holiday to Hawaii with Steven Spielberg rather than attend the premiere of his own 1977 movie, so convinced was he that it would be a failure?

George Lucas—for *Star Wars*

3 "Sunrise, Sunset" is a song that can be found in which 1971 musical?

Fiddler on the Roof

4 Restore the missing vowels and change the spacing to reveal the title of a gritty movie, telling the story of a Michael Caine character returning to his roots in Newcastle upon Tyne:

G TCR TR

Get Carter

5 Which Stanley Kubrick film famously utilized a special technique for filming in candlelight, to avoid the need for traditional film lighting?

Barry Lyndon

6 Which actress played the role of Carrie in the film of the same name?

Sissy Spacek

7 What is the name of the actor who played the world champion, Apollo, in *Rocky*?

Carl Weathers

Robert De Niro
QUESTIONS

1. In how many movies released during the 1970s did Robert De Niro work with director Martin Scorsese?

2. Who is Travis Bickle addressing while he delivers his famous "you talkin' to me?" speech in *Taxi Driver*?

3. What deadly game are Robert De Niro and Christopher Walken made to play in *The Deer Hunter*?

4. Which island did De Niro move to, as preparation for his role in *The Godfather Part II*?

5. Complete the title of this 1971 De Niro film:

   The _____ That Couldn't Shoot Straight

6. *The Last Tycoon*, starring De Niro as the titular tycoon, Monroe Stahr, was based on the unfinished novel of which author?

7. Which 1973 De Niro film features the line, "You don't make up for your sins in church. You do it in the streets…"?

8. What was De Niro's nickname while growing up, based on his thin, pale appearance?

9. De Niro has twin sons from his relationship with which fashion model, the sister of the late designer of the WilliWear line?

Robert De Niro
ANSWERS

1 In how many movies released during the 1970s did Robert De Niro work with director Martin Scorsese?

Three

The three movies are Mean Streets, Taxi Driver, *and* New York, New York. *Scorsese and De Niro have collaborated several times since, as well. De Niro said of Scorsese, "I wish I had that knowledge of movies that he has. He's like an encyclopedia. I could call him up and ask him about a certain movie, and he would know about it. He's seen everything."*

2 Who is Travis Bickle addressing while he delivers his famous "you talkin' to me?" speech in *Taxi Driver*?

Himself—in a mirror

3 What deadly game are Robert De Niro and Christopher Walken made to play in *The Deer Hunter*?

Russian roulette

4 Which island did De Niro move to, as preparation for his role in *The Godfather Part II*?

Sicily

5 Complete the title of this 1971 De Niro film:

The _____ That Couldn't Shoot Straight

Gang

6 *The Last Tycoon*, starring De Niro as the titular tycoon, Monroe Stahr, was based on the unfinished novel of which author?

F. Scott Fitzgerald

7 Which 1973 De Niro film features the line, "You don't make up for your sins in church. You do it in the streets…"?

Mean Streets

8 What was De Niro's nickname while growing up, based on his thin, pale appearance?

Bobby Milk

9 De Niro has twin sons from his relationship with which fashion model, the sister of the late designer of the WilliWear line?

Toukie Smith

Disaster Movies

QUESTIONS

1 The 1974 disaster movie, *The Towering Inferno*, included which legendary screen dancer among its ensemble cast?

2 Who was the only actor or actress to be Oscar-nominated for their role in *The Poseidon Adventure*?

3 What was the cataclysmic event which resulted in the SS Poseidon turning upside down in *The Poseidon Adventure*?

4 The 138-floor tower in *The Towering Inferno* is said to be the tallest in the world, within the fictional world of the movie, but exactly how tall is it?

a. 1,000 feet
b. 1,266 feet
c. 1,688 feet
d. 2,110 feet

5 In 1974, which movie was marketed with the gimmicky "Sensurround" —a technique whereby low frequency sound was played to create a rumbling effect?

6 Which Burt Lancaster movie, released in 1970, went on to be spoofed in both *Airplane!* and *Airplane II: The Sequel*?

7 Which 1978 movie stars Michael Caine as an entomologist who has long been predicting a war between humans and insects?

Disaster Movies

ANSWERS

1 The 1974 disaster movie, *The Towering Inferno*, included which legendary screen dancer among its ensemble cast?

Fred Astaire

Despite making around forty movies, it turned out to be Fred Astaire's only Oscar-nominated performance. Although he did not win the Oscar, he went on to win a BAFTA and Golden Globe for his part in the movie, in which he played the role of Harlee Claiborne.

2 Who was the only actor or actress to be Oscar-nominated for their role in *The Poseidon Adventure*?

Shelley Winters

3 What was the cataclysmic event which resulted in the SS Poseidon turning upside down in *The Poseidon Adventure*?

It was hit by a tidal wave

4 The 138-floor tower in *The Towering Inferno* is said to be the tallest in the world, within the fictional world of the movie, but exactly how tall is it?

a. 1,000 feet
b. 1,266 feet
c. 1,688 feet
d. 2,110 feet

c. 1,688 feet

5 In 1974, which movie was marketed with the gimmicky "Sensurround"—a technique whereby low frequency sound was played to create a rumbling effect?

Earthquake

6 Which Burt Lancaster movie, released in 1970, went on to be spoofed in both *Airplane!* and *Airplane II: The Sequel*?

Airport

7 Which 1978 movie stars Michael Caine as an entomologist who has long been predicting a war between humans and insects?

The Swarm

Based on Music
QUESTIONS

1 For his leading role in which movie did Robert De Niro spend three months learning to play the saxophone?

2 The 1976 release of *A Star Is Born* was a remake. How many times had a movie with the same title and story been previously released?

3 Change one letter in each word below to reveal the name of the 1979 musical comedy which featured the punk rock group The Ramones:

SOCK 'A' DOLL SIGH SCHOWL

4 Who played the part of Esther Hoffman in *A Star Is Born*?

5 Which movie was promoted using the tagline "...Catch it!"?

6 Bob Fosse directed which film that opens with Roy Scheider taking a shower with a cigarette in his mouth?

7 Which 1976 movie stars Irene Cara, Lonette McKee, and Dwan Smith as three sisters aspiring to be famous singers?

Based on Music
ANSWERS

1 For his leading role in which movie did Robert De Niro spend three months learning to play the saxophone?

New York, New York

> *De Niro wanted to ensure his performance looked as authentic as possible. His actual sax playing, however, was dubbed over by veteran jazz musician Georgie Auld, who also played the role of the band leader in the film.*

2 The 1976 release of *A Star Is Born* was a remake. How many times had a movie with the same title and story been previously released?

Twice, in 1937 and 1954

3 Change one letter in each word below to reveal the name of the 1979 musical comedy which featured the punk rock group The Ramones:

SOCK 'A' DOLL SIGH SCHOWL

Rock 'n' Roll High School

4 Who played the part of Esther Hoffman in *A Star Is Born*?

Barbra Streisand

5 Which movie was promoted using the tagline "...Catch it!"?

Saturday Night Fever

6 Bob Fosse directed which film that opens with Roy Scheider taking a shower with a cigarette in his mouth?

All That Jazz

7 Which 1976 movie stars Irene Cara, Lonette McKee, and Dwan Smith as three sisters aspiring to be famous singers?

Sparkle

Comedies 2
QUESTIONS

1. Which Broadway actress, known for her Broadway roles in Sondheim shows, starred opposite Steve Martin in the 1979 comedy *The Jerk*, in a role that he wrote for her?

2. Who starred as Chief Inspector Clouseau in *Revenge of the Pink Panther*, in the actor's final turn in the role before his death in 1980?

3. Clips from which 1942 film, starring Humphrey Bogart, are peppered into the action of the 1972 comedy, *Play It Again, Sam*?

4. Which 1979 film by Monty Python was banned in several European countries following accusations of being blasphemous?

5. Which actor, famous for her role in *The Sound of Music*, played the lead character's girlfriend in the comedy caper *10*?

6. Which film, starring Goldie Hawn and Chevy Chase, featured the theme song *Ready to Take a Chance Again*, which went on to be nominated for Best Original Song at the Oscars?

7. Rearrange the letters below to reveal the name of a 1971 film in which the lead character's daughter runs away from home at the beginning of the movie:

   KING OF FAT (6, 3)

Comedies 2
ANSWERS

1 Which Broadway actress, known for her Broadway roles in Sondheim shows, starred opposite Steve Martin in the 1979 comedy *The Jerk*, in a role that he wrote for her?

Bernadette Peters

> *Martin wrote the role for his then-partner, Peters, who later commented that the script's spontaneity was down to Martin and the film's director sharing a car to work every day, and sharing new jokes. A scene during which Martin's character licks her face was reportedly ad-libbed, and the reaction of Peter was included unedited.*

2 Who starred as Chief Inspector Clouseau in *Revenge of the Pink Panther*, in the actor's final turn in the role before his death in 1980?

Peter Sellars

3 Clips from which 1942 film, starring Humphrey Bogart, are peppered into the action of the 1972 comedy, *Play It Again, Sam*?

Casablanca

4 Which 1979 film by Monty Python was banned in several European countries following accusations of being blasphemous?

Monty Python's Life of Brian

5 Which actor, famous for her role in *The Sound of Music*, played the lead character's girlfriend in the comedy caper *10*?

Julie Andrews

6 Which film, starring Goldie Hawn and Chevy Chase, featured the theme song *Ready to Take a Chance Again*, which went on to be nominated for Best Original Song at the Oscars?

Foul Play

7 Rearrange the letters below to reveal the name of a 1971 film in which the lead character's daughter runs away from home at the beginning of the movie:

KING OF FAT (6, 4)

Taking Off

Pot Luck 2
QUESTIONS

1. Who was nominated for both Best Actor in a Leading Role and for Best Original Screenplay, both for the same film, at the 1977 Oscars?

2. In *Alien*, which Gene Kelly song does Ripley sing to herself while preparing to flush the alien into space?

3. Which 1976 satirical comedy-drama starred Faye Dunaway as news division programming chief Diana Christensen?

4. Which dystopian film ends with the final and somewhat ambiguous line, "I was cured all right"?

5. Which now-five-time Oscar-nominated director was at the helm for the 1975 crime drama, *Dog Day Afternoon*?

6. What was the name of Jodie Foster's character in *Taxi Driver*?

7. In the film series of the same name, what is "Dirty" Harry's full name?

8. Which 1973 sci-fi film, written and directed by Michael Crichton, follows adult guests at an interactive park and went on to inspire a 2016 TV series?

9. George Lucas made his directorial feature-film debut with which 1971 movie, set in a dystopian future in which emotions must be suppressed by drugs?

Pot Luck 2
ANSWERS

1 Who was nominated for both Best Actor in a Leading Role and for Best Original Screenplay, both for the same film, at the 1977 Oscars?

Sylvester Stallone

Both nominations were for Rocky. As an unemployed actor prior to the production of the movie, he refused to sell the script for Rocky unless it was agreed that he would play the lead. The studio eventually agreed, offering him a much lower amount. One of the first things he did with his earnings from the movie was to buy back his dog, which he had been forced to sell a few weeks earlier to help save money.

2 In *Alien*, which Gene Kelly song does Ripley sing to herself while preparing to flush the alien into space?

You Are My Lucky Star

3 Which 1976 satirical comedy-drama starred Faye Dunaway as news division programming chief Diana Christensen?

Network

4 Which dystopian film ends with the final and somewhat ambiguous line, "I was cured all right"?

A Clockwork Orange

5 Which now-five-time Oscar-nominated director was at the helm for the 1975 crime drama, *Dog Day Afternoon*?

Sidney Lumet

6 What was the name of Jodie Foster's character in *Taxi Driver*?

Iris

7 In the film series of the same name, what is "Dirty" Harry's full name?

Inspector Harold Francis Callahan

8 Which 1973 sci-fi film, written and directed by Michael Crichton, follows adult guests at an interactive park and went on to inspire a 2016 TV series?

Westworld

9 George Lucas made his directorial feature-film debut with which 1971 movie, set in a dystopian future in which emotions must be suppressed by drugs?

THX 1138

Francis Ford Coppola
QUESTIONS

1. What illness did Francis Ford Coppola contract as a child that led to him being bedridden for large periods of his childhood?

2. Complete this line from Marlon Brando's Colonel Kurtz in *Apocalypse Now*: "The horror, the _____".

3. In the 1970 movie *Patton*, what does General Patton desperately not want his men to lose their fear of?

4. Which Francis Ford Coppola movie starts with the iconic line, "I believe in America"?

5. Which young actress appeared in all three *Godfather* films, but was uncredited for the first two?

6. Outside film-making and its associated industries, what other business did Francis Ford Coppola move into after buying part of the Inglenook Estate in 1975?

7. Unjumble the following letters to reveal a *Star Wars* actor who appeared in both *The Conversation* and *Apocalypse Now*:

   FRONDS OR HAIR (8, 4)

1 What illness did Francis Ford Coppola contract as a child that led to him being bedridden for large periods of his childhood?

Polio

He contracted polio when he was nine years old. He passed the large amounts of time he spent at home in making his own puppet theatrical shows, and creating 8mm home movies. He later explained that these formative experiences provoked his subsequent interest in feature-film making.

2 Complete this line from Marlon Brando's Colonel Kurtz in *Apocalypse Now*: "The horror, the _____".

Horror

3 In the 1970 movie *Patton*, what does General Patton desperately not want his men to lose their fear of?

Him

4 Which Francis Ford Coppola movie starts with the iconic line, "I believe in America"?

The Godfather

5 Which young actress appeared in all three *Godfather* films, but was uncredited for the first two?

Sofia Coppola

6 Outside film-making and its associated industries, what other business did Francis Ford Coppola move into after buying part of the Inglenook Estate in 1975?

Wine-making

7 Unjumble the following letters to reveal a *Star Wars* actor who appeared in both *The Conversation* and *Apocalypse Now*:

FRONDS OR HAIR (8, 4)

Harrison Ford

Oscar Actresses
QUESTIONS

1. Ellen Burstyn won the Best Actress Oscar in 1975 for her role as Alice Hyatt in which American comedy drama film?

2. After her Oscar win in 1972 for *Klute*, which actress wrapped up her short speech with the words "There's a great deal to say and I'm not going to say it tonight. I would just like to really thank you very much."?

3. *Blazing Saddles* was nominated for three Oscars, one of which was for Best Supporting Actress. Although she did not win, who was this nominee?

4. Which British star won the Best Actress Oscar at the 1970 ceremony for her role in *The Prime of Miss Jean Brodie*?

5. Beatrice Straight won the Best Supporting Actress Oscar in 1977, when she was in her 60s, for which satirical film?

6. American actress Louise Fletcher won her only Oscar in 1976, for which psychological comedy drama?

7. How many Oscars did the actress Meryl Streep win during the 1970s?

Oscars Actresses

1 Ellen Burstyn won the Best Actress Oscar in 1975 for her role as Alice Hyatt in which American comedy drama film?

Alice Doesn't Live Here Anymore

Martin Scorsese directed this film in which Burstyn plays a mother taking her son across the United States in search of a better life. She was nominated for an Oscar a total of four times throughout the 1970s, for The Last Picture Show, The Exorcist, Alice Doesn't Live Here Anymore, and Same Time, Next Year.

2 After her Oscar win in 1972 for *Klute*, which actress wrapped up her short speech with the words "There's a great deal to say and I'm not going to say it tonight. I would just like to really thank you very much."?

Jane Fonda

3 *Blazing Saddles* was nominated for three Oscars, one of which was for Best Supporting Actress. Although she did not win, who was this nominee?

Madeline Kahn

4 Which British star won the Best Actress Oscar at the 1970 ceremony for her role in *The Prime of Miss Jean Brodie*?

Maggie Smith

5 Beatrice Straight won the Best Supporting Actress Oscar in 1977, when she was in her 60s, for which satirical film?

Network

6 American actress Louise Fletcher won her only Oscar in 1976, for which psychological comedy drama?

One Flew Over the Cuckoo's Nest

7 How many Oscars did the actress Meryl Streep win during the 1970s?

One, for *Kramer vs. Kramer*

Children's Movies
QUESTIONS

1. Which Gene Wilder character first appears in a 1971 movie limping along with a walking stick, before unexpectedly tumbling into a somersault?

2. In *The Muppet Movie*, what role does "Animal" play in the band?

3. Which Disney animated film tells the story of a family of Parisian cats trying to make their way home?

4. Which 1978 musical adventure film, which has an almost entirely African-American cast, is a reimagining of *The Wizard of Oz*?

5. Telling the story of a boy who is shipwrecked on a desert island with a wild horse, which 1979 movie is based on a 1941 children's novel of the same name?

6. In the original 1976 *Freaky Friday*, who plays the daughter who ends up swapping places with her mother?

7. In Disney's anthropomorphic animal version of the *Robin Hood* story, what type of animal is Maid Marian?

Children's Movies

ANSWERS

1 Which Gene Wilder character first appears in a 1971 movie limping along with a walking stick, before unexpectedly tumbling into a somersault?

Willy Wonka

Wilder said that he would only accept the role in Willy Wonka & the Chocolate Factory *if he was allowed to limp and then somersault when he first meets the children. When director Mel Stuart asked him why, Wilder responded that it meant "from that time on, no one will know if I'm lying or telling the truth."*

2 In *The Muppet Movie*, what role does "Animal" play in the band?

Drummer

3 Which Disney animated film tells the story of a family of Parisian cats trying to make their way home?

The Aristocats

4 Which 1978 musical adventure film, which has an almost entirely African-American cast, is a reimagining of *The Wizard of Oz*?

The Wiz

5 Telling the story of a boy who is shipwrecked on a desert island with a wild horse, which 1979 movie is based on a 1941 children's novel of the same name?

The Black Stallion

6 In the original 1976 *Freaky Friday*, who plays the daughter who ends up swapping places with her mother?

Jodie Foster

7 In Disney's anthropomorphic animal version of the *Robin Hood* story, what type of animal is Maid Marian?

Fox

Out of This World 2
QUESTIONS

1 Who was the director of *Close Encounters of the Third Kind*, which was based on a full-length film he had developed aged 17?

2 In *Escape from the Planet of the Apes*, released in 1971, who played the role of Zira?

3 What is the surname of the character played by John Hurt in *Alien*, from whose chest the eponymous beast emerges?

4 Change one letter in each word below to reveal the name of a 1976 film starring David Bowie as an alien seeking water for his home planet:

TIE MAY WOO FALL SO GARTH

5 Which 1971 film, whose title features the name of the closest galaxy to the Milky Way, examines the hypothetical arrival of a deadly alien pathogen to our planet?

6 Which novel by Kurt Vonnegut was adapted into a 1972 film of the same name, starring Michael Sacks as the protagonist Billy Pilgrim?

7 On which fictional planet was Superman born, which is depicted in the 1978 film starring Marlon Brando as the titular character's father?

Out of This World 2

ANSWERS

1 Who was the director of *Close Encounters of the Third Kind*, which was based on a full-length film he had developed aged 17?

Steven Spielberg

Reportedly first inspired by a meteor shower he witnessed as a child, Spielberg had begun working on a UFO-focused film in his teenage years. He had created the film Firelight *in 1964—from which many* Close Encounters *scenes are closely drawn—earning a profit of one dollar against his $500 budget.*

2 In *Escape from the Planet of the Apes*, released in 1971, who played the role of Zira?

Kim Hunter

3 What is the surname of the character played by John Hurt in *Alien*, from whose chest the eponymous beast emerges?

Kane

4 Change one letter in each word below to reveal the name of a 1976 film starring David Bowie as an alien seeking water for his home planet:

TIE MAY WOO FALL SO GARTH

The Man Who Fell to Earth

5 Which 1971 film, whose title features the name of the closest galaxy to the Milky Way, examines the hypothetical arrival of a deadly alien pathogen to our planet?

The Andromeda Strain

6 Which novel by Kurt Vonnegut was adapted into a 1972 film of the same name, starring Michael Sacks as the protagonist Billy Pilgrim?

Slaughterhouse-Five

7 On which fictional planet was Superman born, which is depicted in the 1978 film starring Marlon Brando as the titular character's father?

Krypton

Dustin Hoffman
QUESTIONS

1 In an iconic scene of which 1976 Dustin Hoffman movie is the line "Is it safe?" asked more than once, receiving inconsistent answers?

2 Unjumble the following letters to reveal the actress who played opposite Hoffman as his wife in *Kramer vs. Kramer*:

MEREST REPLY (5, 6)

3 Which Dustin Hoffman film has a deleted scene featuring an appearance by June Brown, who would later play Dot Cotton in the long-running BBC soap, *EastEnders*?

4 Which acerbic comedian did Hoffman play in the 1974 biographical drama, *Lenny*?

5 Which Hoffman film had the tagline "The most devastating detective story of the century"?

6 Which of these is *not* the title of a Dustin Hoffman film of the 1970s?

a. *Papillon*
b. *Straight Time*
c. *Three Days of the Condor*
d. *Straw Dogs*

7 How old is Hoffman's character, Jack Crabb, in the opening scene of *Little Big Man*?

a. 88 years old
b. 99 years old
c. 110 years old
d. 121 years old

Dustin Hoffman
ANSWERS

1 In an iconic scene of which 1976 Dustin Hoffman movie is the line "Is it safe?" asked more than once, receiving inconsistent answers?

Marathon Man

> *The line is spoken by Dr. Szell, played by Laurence Olivier, as he tortures Babe, played by Hoffman. In one scene Hoffman's character has been kept awake for three nights. When Olivier asked him what he had done to prepare, Hoffman told him he'd simply stayed awake for three nights himself—to which Olivier asked "why don't you just try acting?".*

2 Unjumble the following letters to reveal the actress who played opposite Hoffman as his wife in *Kramer vs. Kramer*:

MEREST REPLY (5, 6)

Meryl Streep

3 Which Dustin Hoffman film has a deleted scene featuring an appearance by June Brown, who would later play Dot Cotton in the long-running BBC soap, *EastEnders*?

Straw Dogs

4 Which acerbic comedian did Hoffman play in the 1974 biographical drama, *Lenny*?

Lenny Bruce

5 Which Hoffman film had the tagline "The most devastating detective story of the century"?

All the President's Men

6 Which of these is *not* the title of a Dustin Hoffman film of the 1970s?

a. *Papillon*
b. *Straight Time*
c. *Three Days of the Condor*
d. *Straw Dogs*

c. *Three Days of the Condor*

7 How old is Hoffman's character, Jack Crabb, in the opening scene of *Little Big Man*?

a. 88 years old
b. 99 years old
c. 110 years old
d. 121 years old

d. 121 years old

Award Winners 2
QUESTIONS

1. Which award-winning 1970s movie opens with the line, "Willkommen, Bienvenue, Welcome"?

2. George Lucas directed which movie, produced by Francis Ford Coppola, that was nominated for the Academy Award for Best Picture but lost out to *The Sting*?

3. In what year at the BAFTA Film Awards were Jack Nicholson, Albert Finney, Gene Hackman, and Al Pacino the four nominees in the Best Actor category, one of them for two movies?

4. Which 1969 book by Robin Moore was adapted into a film of the same name that went on to win the Academy Award for Best Picture winner at the 1972 ceremony?

5. Which film, that won Best Picture at the Oscars in 1970, featured the hit single *Everybody's Talkin'*?

6. In 1979's *Kramer vs. Kramer*, what are the titular couple's first names?

7. Which was the first movie to feature African-American nominees for both Best Actor and Best Actress Oscars?

Award Winners 2
ANSWERS

1 Which award-winning 1970s movie opens with the line, "Willkommen, Bienvenue, Welcome"?

Cabaret

The movie won eight Academy Awards out of its ten nominations, and seven BAFTA Film awards out of its eleven nominations. Although it is based on the Broadway musical of the same name, it has some significant differences, including the change of nationality of the lead character, Sally, from British to American.

2 George Lucas directed which movie, produced by Francis Ford Coppola, that was nominated for the Academy Award for Best Picture but lost out to *The Sting*?

American Graffiti

3 In what year at the BAFTA Film Awards were Jack Nicholson, Albert Finney, Gene Hackman, and Al Pacino the four nominees in the Best Actor category, one of them for two movies?

1975 (for films released in 1974)

4 Which 1969 book by Robin Moore was adapted into a film of the same name that went on to win the Academy Award for Best Picture winner at the 1972 ceremony?

The French Connection

5 Which film, that won Best Picture at the Oscars in 1970, featured the hit single *Everybody's Talkin'*?

Midnight Cowboy

6 In 1979's *Kramer vs. Kramer*, what are the titular couple's first names?

Ted and Joanna

7 Which was the first movie to feature African-American nominees for both Best Actor and Best Actress Oscars?

Sounder

Star Wars 2
QUESTIONS

1 What is the name of the visual effects company which was founded by George Lucas specifically to work on *Star Wars*?

2 While walking through a Rebel base, which character asks "Will somebody get this big walking carpet out of my way?"

3 Unjumble the letters below to reveal the name of the ship which Luke Skywalker describes on first sight as "a piece of junk":

MINE MALFUNCTION HELL (3, 10, 6)

4 What kind of ship does Luke Skywalker fly during the final assault on the Death Star?

5 What do Han Solo and Luke Skywalker disguise themselves as while they attempt to rescue Princess Leia?

6 What is notable about the sunset which Luke looks out at near the start of the film?

7 Who is the only actor who was nominated for an Oscar for their role in *Star Wars*?

Star Wars 2
ANSWERS

1 What is the name of the visual effects company which was founded by George Lucas specifically to work on *Star Wars*?

Industrial Light & Magic

The company's ground-breaking miniature and blue screen work won it an Oscar and ensured it went on to become a visual-effects powerhouse. The company continues to dominate the special effects industry, although it was subsequently acquired by Disney in 2012.

2 While walking through a Rebel base, which character asks "Will somebody get this big walking carpet out of my way?"

Princess Leia

3 Unjumble the letters below to reveal the name of the ship which Luke Skywalker describes on first sight as "a piece of junk":

MINE MALFUNCTION HELL (3, 10, 6)

The Millennium Falcon

4 What kind of ship does Luke Skywalker fly during the final assault on the Death Star?

An X-Wing

5 What do Han Solo and Luke Skywalker disguise themselves as while they attempt to rescue Princess Leia?

Stormtroopers

6 What is notable about the sunset which Luke looks out at near the start of the film?

There are two suns

7 Who is the only actor who was nominated for an Oscar for their role in *Star Wars*?

Alec Guinness

The Oscars
QUESTIONS

1 Which on-stage presenter broke into dance before presenting the Best Documentary Feature Oscar in 1970?

2 Which actor, who later had a major role in *Star Wars*, was nominated for the Best Actor Oscar in 1971?

3 Which veteran film star was presented with an Honorary Oscar by Frank Sinatra at the 1970 ceremony?

4 Unjumble the following letters to reveal the veteran movie editor, known for her work with Martin Scorsese, who was nominated for Best Film Editing for the first time in 1971 for *Woodstock*:

MOCKS HEATHEN MORAL (6, 11)

5 In most years the Academy awards the Jean Hersholt Humanitarian Award for an individual's "outstanding contributions to humanitarian causes". Which actor and political activist was given the prize in 1971?

6 Jerry Goldsmith won Best Original Score at the Oscars in 1977 for the "unholy" score to which film, featuring chanting voices?

7 In which year of the 1970s did comedian and talk-show host Johnny Carson first host the Oscars ceremony?

The Oscars
ANSWERS

1 Which on-stage presenter broke into dance before presenting the Best Documentary Feature Oscar in 1970?

Fred Astaire

Presenting with Bob Hope, Astaire came out of retirement and treated a delighted audience to a preplanned routine, reinforcing why the-then 71-year-old was still considered the greatest dancer in film history.

2 Which actor, who later had a major role in *Star Wars*, was nominated for the Best Actor Oscar in 1971?

James Earl Jones

3 Which veteran film star was presented with an Honorary Oscar by Frank Sinatra at the 1970 ceremony?

Cary Grant

4 Unjumble the following letters to reveal the veteran movie editor, known for her work with Martin Scorsese, who was nominated for Best Film Editing for the first time in 1971 for *Woodstock*:

MOCKS HEATHEN MORAL (6, 11)

Thelma Schoonmaker

5 In most years the Academy awards the Jean Hersholt Humanitarian Award for an individual's "outstanding contributions to humanitarian causes". Which actor and political activist was given the prize in 1971?

Frank Sinatra

6 Jerry Goldsmith won Best Original Score at the Oscars in 1977 for the "unholy" score to which film, featuring chanting voices?

The Omen

7 In which year of the 1970s did comedian and talk-show host Johnny Carson first host the Oscars ceremony?

1979

TV SHOWS

In the 70s, game shows spread like live-audience applause, medical dramas made their debut STAT, and crime dramas dominated TV screens globally. The 1970s saw a shift away from the wholesome family sitcom and more towards socially forward, urban content that gave you the skinny on life. By this era, most television programs were being broadcast in color, and color TV sets became more reliable, less expensive and far more widespread.

Now for The Six Million Dollar question: Are you a regular Columbo when it comes to 70s TV trivia? Well gather your Brady Bunch together, invite over The Odd Couple, and it'll be Good Times and Happy Days as you Kung Fu your way through this M*A*S*H up of 70s TV trivia!

1. Which 14-year-old guest appeared on an episode of the show in 1972, and performed as part of a famous group of brothers?

2. What was Sonny's surname, which was sometimes also taken by Cher during their marriage?

3. What was the primary reason for the show coming to an end in 1974?

4. Which actor and comedian who later starred in the movie *The Jerk* was credited as a writer on the show, and regularly appeared in sketches?

5. Can you change one letter in each word below to reveal the name of a song written by Sonny that was frequently heard during the show's opening sequences?

   SHE BEST GODS IN

6. What was the title of the song performed by the couple at the end of each episode, which had been originally released in 1965?

7. At which prestigious 1974 awards show did Cher win "Best TV Actress in a Comedy or Musical" for *The Sonny & Cher Comedy Hour*?

1 Which 14-year-old guest appeared on an episode of the show in 1972, and performed as part of a famous group of brothers?

Michael Jackson, as part of The Jackson 5

The group performed their song Looking' Through The Windows, *from their just-released album of the same name. In a skit, Sonny asked Jackson what he wanted to be when he grew up. The young singer suggested he might be "a jet pilot, an astronaut, or the governor of Georgia".*

2 What was Sonny's surname, which was sometimes also taken by Cher during their marriage?

Bono

3 What was the primary reason for the show coming to an end in 1974?

The couple's divorce

4 Which actor and comedian who later starred in the movie *The Jerk* was credited as a writer on the show, and regularly appeared in sketches?

Steve Martin

5 Can you change one letter in each word below to reveal the name of a song written by Sonny that was frequently heard during the show's opening sequences?

SHE BEST GODS IN

The Beat Goes On

6 What was the title of the song performed by the couple at the end of each episode, which had been originally released in 1965?

I Got You, Babe

7 At which prestigious 1974 awards show did Cher win "Best TV Actress in a Comedy or Musical" for *The Sonny & Cher Comedy Hour*?

The Golden Globes

1. Which 1970s musical sitcom has a theme tune called *C'mon, Get Happy*, used from its second season onwards?

2. "Come and knock on our door" was the first line in the opening theme to which US sitcom, based on the British show *Man About the House*?

3. Which iconic US sitcom has a theme tune that features the lyric "Goodbye gray skies, hello blue"?

4. Which show's narrative theme tune is accompanied by a title card that shows the fictional family members in a three-by-three grid, each with their own moving headshot?

5. Rearrange the letters below to reveal the name of a US sitcom whose theme song was performed by American singer Jack Jones:

   TO LEAVE BOTH (3, 4, 4)

6. What is the name of the theme tune from *The Jeffersons*, featuring a gospel choir and which was later covered by both Beyonce and Sammy Davis Jr.?

7. What is the name of the theme song in *Laverne & Shirley*, played after the pair have performed a hopscotch routine during the opening credits?

Theme Tunes

ANSWERS

1 Which 1970s musical sitcom has a theme tune called *C'mon, Get Happy*, used from its second season onwards?

The Partridge Family

The show's original theme tune had been titled When We're Singin', *but was re-recorded with new lyrics to create the show's much more well-known theme. Much of the music from the sitcom featured session musicians from a collective known as "The Wrecking Crew", who had also provided music for Cher, The Carpenters, and Simon & Garfunkel.*

2 "Come and knock on our door" was the first line in the opening theme to which US sitcom, based on the British show *Man About the House*?

Three's Company

3 Which iconic US sitcom has a theme tune that features the lyric "Goodbye gray skies, hello blue"?

Happy Days

4 Which show's narrative theme tune is accompanied by a title card that shows the fictional family members in a three-by-three grid, each with their own moving headshot?

The Brady Bunch

5 Rearrange the letters below to reveal the name of a US sitcom whose theme song was performed by American singer Jack Jones:

TO LEAVE BOTH (3, 4, 4)

The Love Boat

6 What is the name of the theme tune from *The Jeffersons*, featuring a gospel choir and which was later covered by both Beyonce and Sammy Davis Jr.?

Movin' On Up

7 What is the name of the theme song in *Laverne & Shirley*, played after the pair have performed a hopscotch routine during the opening credits?

Making Our Dreams Come True

1. Which series, that premiered in 1978, stars Bill Bixby and Lou Ferrigno as different sides of the same man?

2. In which century did the character of Buck Rogers wake up after a malfunction on his ship?

3. On which ship featured in the title of a 1970s TV show would you find Lieutenant Starbuck?

4. What adjective is used to describe Spider-Man in the title of a 1977 show?

   a. Amazing
   b. Fantastic
   c. Incredible
   d. Unbelievable

5. What character, featured in the title of a 1970s Saturday-morning show, is a superhero who was granted powers by Solomon, Hercules, Atlas, Zeus, Achilles, and Mercury?

6. Can you name the actor who played Steve Austin, the man referred to in the title of *The Six Million Dollar Man*?

7. During episodes of *Wonder Woman*, what weapon was wielded on-screen by the titular character?

1 Which series, that premiered in 1978, stars Bill Bixby and Lou Ferrigno as different sides of the same man?

The Incredible Hulk

Based on The Hulk *comic strip by Stan Lee and Jack Kirby, the opening credits show the Hulk lifting a car. During filming this was intended to be actually lifted by a steel cable, but it snapped. The shoot was running late so, rather than waiting for it to be repaired, Ferrigno lifted up the car himself and rolled it down the hill.*

2 In which century did the character of Buck Rogers wake up after a malfunction on his ship?

The 25th century, in *Buck Rogers in the 25th Century*

3 On which ship featured in the title of a 1970s TV show would you find Lieutenant Starbuck?

Battlestar Galactica

4 What adjective is used to describe Spider-Man in the title of a 1977 show?

a. Amazing
b. Fantastic
c. Incredible
d. Unbelievable

a. Amazing—in *The Amazing Spider-Man*

5 What character, featured in the title of a 1970s Saturday-morning show, is a superhero who was granted powers by Solomon, Hercules, Atlas, Zeus, Achilles, and Mercury?

Shazam!

6 Can you name the actor who played Steve Austin, the man referred to in the title of *The Six Million Dollar Man*?

Lee Majors

7 During episodes of *Wonder Woman*, what weapon was wielded on-screen by the titular character?

The Lasso of Truth—a.k.a. the Magic Lasso or Golden Perfect

1. Which TV show's opening credits feature the main character saying "Gentlemen, you are about to enter the fascinating sphere of police work: the world of forensic medicine"?

2. *The Streets of San Francisco* follows two homicide detectives, played by Karl Malden and which future winner of the Best Actor Oscar?

3. Crime drama *CHiPs* features two motorcycle officers patrolling in which US state, represented by one of the letters in the show's title?

4. Which crime fighting show is home to the characters of Huggy Bear and Captain Harold Dobey?

5. Played by John Forsythe, what was the name of the disembodied voice which would give three "Angels" a new mission each week?

6. In a series that premiered in 1979, what was the surname of Jonathan and Jennifer, a globetrotting married couple who solved mysteries wherever they went?

7. Peter Falk provided his own wardrobe for Columbo's iconic outfit, in the show of the same name. What shabby item was he famous for wearing?

1 Which TV show's opening credits feature the main character saying "Gentlemen, you are about to enter the fascinating sphere of police work: the world of forensic medicine"?

Quincy, M.E.

> *The show was inspired by former FBI agent Marshall Houts's book,* Where Death Delights. *It became the first detective show to regularly feature in-depth forensic evidence, which would later become a hallmark of many police dramas.*

2 *The Streets of San Francisco* follows two homicide detectives, played by Karl Malden and which future winner of the Best Actor Oscar?

Michael Douglas

3 Crime drama *CHiPs* features two motorcycle officers patrolling in which US state, represented by one of the letters in the show's title?

California—CHiPs stands for "California Highway Patrol"

4 Which crime fighting show is home to the characters of Huggy Bear and Captain Harold Dobey?

Starsky & Hutch

5 Played by John Forsythe, what was the name of the disembodied voice which would give three "Angels" a new mission each week?

Charlie—in Charlie's Angels

6 In a series that premiered in 1979, what was the surname of Jonathan and Jennifer, a globetrotting married couple who solved mysteries wherever they went?

Hart—in Hart to Hart

7 Peter Falk provided his own wardrobe for Columbo's iconic outfit, in the show of the same name. What shabby item was he famous for wearing?

A raincoat

UK Comedy 1
QUESTIONS

1. Which comedy show, which ran until 1974, is credited with inspiring the use of the term "spam" for unwanted electronic communications?

2. In *Fawlty Towers*, what kind of salad is an American guest famously unable to get the hotel kitchen to make?

3. What was the name of the seaside town notionally defended by *Dad's Army*?

4. *On the Buses* ran on ITV for seven series after having been previously rejected by the BBC. What was the name of the miserable bus inspector played by actor Stephen Lewis?

5. Unjumble the letters below to reveal the name of one of the two lead actors in *The Good Life*, a BBC sitcom which originally aired from 1975 until 1978:

RARE RICH BIRDS (7, 6)

6. Which sitcom, named after an undesirable feature of poorly ventilated housing, starred Don Warrington as Philip Smith?

7. Change one letter per word below to reveal the title of a British sitcom which ran for a staggering 31 series, after first premiering in 1973:

CAST ON SHE HUMMER WIFE

1 Which comedy show, which ran until 1974, is credited with inspiring the use of the term "spam" for unwanted electronic communications?

Monty Python's Flying Circus

The "Spam Sketch" involved a cafe menu where every single item on the menu came with the branded canned meat, Spam, including "egg + spam", "egg bacon + spam", and "spam spam spam egg + spam". So just as the unwanted spam came with everything in the sketch, so people are "spammed" with unwanted emails. Canned Spam is still available today, in over 100 countries worldwide.

2 In *Fawlty Towers*, what kind of salad is an American guest famously unable to get the hotel kitchen to make?

Waldorf salad

3 What was the name of the seaside town notionally defended by *Dad's Army*?

Walmington-on-Sea

4 *On the Buses* ran on ITV for seven series after having been previously rejected by the BBC. What was the name of the miserable bus inspector played by actor Stephen Lewis?

Cyril "Blakey" Blake

5 Unjumble the letters below to reveal the name of one of the two lead actors in *The Good Life*, a BBC sitcom which originally aired from 1975 until 1978:

RARE RICH BIRDS (7, 6)

Richard Briers

6 Which sitcom, named after an undesirable feature of poorly ventilated housing, starred Don Warrington as Philip Smith?

Rising Damp

7 Change one letter per word below to reveal the title of a British sitcom which ran for a staggering 31 series, after first premiering in 1973:

CAST ON SHE HUMMER WIFE

Last of the Summer Wine

1. What is the name of the *Sesame Street* character, introduced to the show in 1972, depicted as a vampire who delights in numbers?

2. Which Jim Henson show was broadcast regularly from 1976, featuring the existing *Sesame Street* character Kermit the Frog alongside the newly created Miss Piggy?

3. Which supernatural Archie Comics property was turned into an animated series that aired from 1970 to 1974, later being remade in the 1990s as a live-action show starring Melissa Joan Hart in the title role?

4. Which London Underground station lends its name to a fictional bear, who appeared in a stop-motion BBC series of the same name which ran from 1976 until 1980?

5. By what one-word name is the DC Comics character Captain Marvel also known, which then became the title of an animated series which aired from 1974 to 1976?

6. The character of Josephine McCoy fronts a fictional band in which 1970 animated TV series, with a name based on its central character?

7. The cartoon series, *Scooby-Doo, Where Are You!*, sees the protagonists driving around in a brightly colored van—but what is the name of that van?

1 What is the name of the *Sesame Street* character, introduced to the show in 1972, depicted as a vampire who delights in numbers?

Count von Count

The character first appeared in a 1972 episode alongside the established characters of Bert and Ernie, dismantling a pyramid so that he could count how many blocks it contains. Belvedere Castle in Central Park, New York, was filmed to create the exterior film of the Count's castle that was used on the show.

2 Which Jim Henson show was broadcast regularly from 1976, featuring the existing *Sesame Street* character Kermit the Frog alongside the newly created Miss Piggy?

The Muppet Show

3 Which supernatural Archie Comics property was turned into an animated series that aired from 1970 to 1974, later being remade in the 1990s as a live-action show starring Melissa Joan Hart in the title role?

Sabrina the Teenage Witch

4 Which London Underground station lends its name to a fictional bear, who appeared in a stop-motion BBC series of the same name which ran from 1976 until 1980?

Paddington

5 By what one-word name is the DC Comics character Captain Marvel also known, which then became the title of an animated series which aired from 1974 to 1976?

Shazam

6 The character of Josephine McCoy fronts a fictional band in which 1970 animated TV series, with a name based on its central character?

Josie and the Pussycats

7 The cartoon series, *Scooby-Doo, Where Are You!*, sees the protagonists driving around in a brightly colored van—but what is the name of that van?

Mystery Machine

US Soaps

1. Launching on January 5, 1970, and then running for over four decades, which ABC soap has a title that is often shortened to *AMC*?

2. Which long-running soap opera, screened throughout the 1970s, was the first US daytime show to feature an interracial relationship?

3. Change one letter in each word below to reveal the name of a soap opera that was broadcast live until 1975, when it switched to a recorded one-hour format:

   IS TOE WOULD BURNS

4. Which long-running show features characters that include Ruby Anderson, Joe Kelly, Lila Quartermaine, and Gail Baldwin?

5. Which soap has a storyline that was dominated in the first half of the 1970s by the murder of character Stanley Norris?

6. Unjumble the letters below to reveal the title of a show, first broadcast in 1975, which revolves around the trials of an Irish-American family in Washington Heights, Manhattan:

   HAY PERSON (5, 4)

7. Coming to an end in 1973 after almost 1,500 episodes, which soap shared its name with a 1955 movie and the song that the movie popularized, later featured on the soundtrack to *Grease*?

1. Launching on January 5, 1970, and then running for over four decades, which ABC soap has a title that is often shortened to *AMC*?

All My Children

Set in the upscale Pine Valley, Philadelphia, the show was unusual for its inclusion of storylines based around the Vietnam War, which had not previously been discussed in any depth in US drama. A 1972 protest speech by the character Ruth Martin won actress Mary Fickett the first Emmy Award to be given to a soap star.

2. Which long-running soap opera, screened throughout the 1970s, was the first US daytime show to feature an interracial relationship?

Days of Our Lives

3. Change one letter in each word below to reveal the name of a soap opera that was broadcast live until 1975, when it switched to a recorded one-hour format:

IS TOE WOULD BURNS

As the World Turns

4. Which long-running show features characters that include Ruby Anderson, Joe Kelly, Lila Quartermaine, and Gail Baldwin?

General Hospital

5. Which soap has a storyline that was dominated in the first half of the 1970s by the murder of character Stanley Norris?

Guiding Light

6. Unjumble the letters below to reveal the title of a show, first broadcast in 1975, which revolves around the trials of an Irish-American family in Washington Heights, Manhattan:

HAY PERSON (5, 4)

Ryan's Hope

7. Coming to an end in 1973 after almost 1,500 episodes, which soap shared its name with a 1955 movie and the song that the movie popularized, later featured on the soundtrack to *Grease*?

Love Is a Many Splendored Thing

1. Which US game show first debuted in its modern form in 1972, and was then presented by Bob Barker for the next 35 years?

2. Which amateur talent show was named after a percussion instrument that was struck if any contender was so bad they needed to be stopped immediately?

3. In which game show does the contestant in the lead sometimes get to participate in an "Instant Bargain" in which they can buy prizes using some of their accumulated score?

4. What catchphrase is used to invite members of the audience to play *The Price Is Right*?

5. First aired in 1976, which game show features families trying to guess the answers to survey questions that have been asked to 100 people?

6. Which US panel game show, where contestants aim to fill in the blanks in answers given by celebrities to certain questions, is known in the UK as *Blankety Blank* and in Australia as *Blankety Blanks*?

7. What is the name of the cultural icon who hosted *The $10,000 Pyramid* from its 1973 launch and then on throughout the rest of the 1970s? The show became *The $20,000 Pyramid* from 1976.

1. Which US game show first debuted in its modern form in 1972, and was then presented by Bob Barker for the next 35 years?

The Price Is Right

Despite various name changes, the show is the longest-running game show of all time. Originally broadcast from 1956 to 1965, it was one of the few shows to survive the public revelation in the late 1950s that most other game shows were fixed so that the producers knew in advance who would win. It relaunched in 1972 with a heavily revised format, and still runs today.

2. Which amateur talent show was named after a percussion instrument that was struck if any contender was so bad they needed to be stopped immediately?

The Gong Show

3. In which game show does the contestant in the lead sometimes get to participate in an "Instant Bargain" in which they can buy prizes using some of their accumulated score?

Sale of the Century

4. What catchphrase is used to invite members of the audience to play *The Price Is Right*?

"Come on down!"

5. First aired in 1976, which game show features families trying to guess the answers to survey questions that have been asked to 100 people?

Family Feud—or Family Fortunes in the UK version

6. Which US panel game show, where contestants aim to fill in the blanks in answers given by celebrities to certain questions, is known in the UK as *Blankety Blank* and in Australia as *Blankety Blanks*?

Match Game

7. What is the name of the cultural icon who hosted *The $10,000 Pyramid* from its 1973 launch and then on throughout the rest of the 1970s? The show became *The $20,000 Pyramid* from 1976.

Dick Clark

1. What is the title of the historical Western series set in Minnesota, based on a series of books by Laura Ingalls Wilder, which aired from 1974 for almost a decade?

2. Which action-adventure medical drama focused on firefighter-paramedics, which originally ran from 1972 to 1977, has an exclamation mark in its title?

3. Which country had the first of many victories at the 1970 *Eurovision Song Contest*, winning with Dana's *All Kinds of Everything*?

4. What paranormal TV series, first broadcast in 1972, shares its name with a 1999 film starring Bruce Willis?

5. David Carradine stars as Shaolin monk Kwai Chang Caine in which series that has the same name as a well-known martial art?

6. Set in the fictional department store Grace Brothers, which British sitcom has a title which is also a question regularly asked by the characters in the show?

7. Change one letter in each word below to reveal the name of a series, broadcast in the UK throughout the 1970s, in which celebrities were invited to recall major life events:

THIN AS TOUR WIFE

Pot Luck 1

ANSWERS

1 What is the title of the historical Western series set in Minnesota, based on a series of books by Laura Ingalls Wilder, which aired from 1974 for almost a decade?

Little House on the Prairie

The TV series was launched with a two-hour pilot movie, which closely followed the plot of Wilder's book of the same name—which in turn was based on her own life story as part of a rural family living in the 1870s USA. The pilot was directed by Michael Landon, who accepted the offer to take the helm after he was promised a lead role in return. He wore four-inch lifts throughout the series, so he would literally tower over the rest of the family.

2 Which action-adventure medical drama focused on firefighter-paramedics, which originally ran from 1972 to 1977, has an exclamation mark in its title?

Emergency!

3 Which country had the first of many victories at the 1970 *Eurovision Song Contest*, winning with Dana's *All Kinds of Everything*?

Ireland

4 What paranormal TV series, first broadcast in 1972, shares its name with a 1999 film starring Bruce Willis?

The Sixth Sense

5 David Carradine stars as Shaolin monk Kwai Chang Caine in which series that has the same name as a well-known martial art?

Kung Fu

6 Set in the fictional department store Grace Brothers, which British sitcom has a title which is also a question regularly asked by the characters in the show?

Are You Being Served?

7 Change one letter in each word below to reveal the name of a series, broadcast in the UK throughout the 1970s, in which celebrities were invited to recall major life events:

THIN AS TOUR WIFE

This Is Your Life

1. In which fictional British town, based on the real-life city of Salford, is the world's longest-running TV soap opera, *Coronation Street*, set?

2. Which British soap, named after a type of road junction, was set in a fictional Birmingham motel?

3. Why were there no daytime British soap operas until the 1970s?

4. What is the title of the medical soap opera which ran in the UK from 1972 to 1979 that shares its name with a still-running US medical show that launched in 1963?

5. Rearrange the letters below to reveal the original name of a long-running soap opera set in Yorkshire, first broadcast in 1972:

   ELM FRAME DREAM (9, 4)

6. The BBC sitcom *Pobol y Cwm* first aired in 1974, and is the longest-running TV soap opera broadcast in which British language?

7. What is the name of the fictional pub in *Coronation Street*, into which a lorry crashed in a 1979 episode?

1 In which fictional British town, based on the real-life city of Salford, is the world's longest-running TV soap opera, *Coronation Street*, set?

Weatherfield

> *Despite having switched to color broadcasts by 1970, industrial disputes on* Coronation Street *led to a "Color Strike" from late 1970 to early 1971, in which technicians working on the show refused to use the "new" color TV equipment and so the show had to be broadcast in black-and-white. Many viewers were oblivious to this, however, since color TV sets did not outnumber black-and-white ones until 1976.*

2 Which British soap, named after a type of road junction, was set in a fictional Birmingham motel?

Crossroads

3 Why were there no daytime British soap operas until the 1970s?

None of the British TV channels had previously broadcast any programming during the times that daytime soap operas were later added

4 What is the title of the medical soap opera which ran in the UK from 1972 to 1979 that shares its name with a still-running US medical show that launched in 1963?

General Hospital

5 Rearrange the letters below to reveal the original name of a long-running soap opera set in Yorkshire, first broadcast in 1972:

ELM FRAME DREAM (9, 4)

Emmerdale Farm

6 The BBC sitcom *Pobol y Cwm* first aired in 1974, and is the longest-running TV soap opera broadcast in which British language?

Welsh

7 What is the name of the fictional pub in *Coronation Street*, into which a lorry crashed in a 1979 episode?

Rovers Return Inn

1. What was *Saturday Night Live*'s original title, used from its launch in 1975 through until 1977?

2. Which characters, played by John Belushi and Dan Ackroyd, made their debut on the episode of January 17, 1976?

3. Which comedian was the host of the launch episode of *Saturday Night Live*?

4. Unjumble the letters below to reveal one of the seven original *Saturday Night Live* cast members, known for performing the characters of Emily Litella and Roseanne Roseannadanna:

   DEAR DARLING (5, 6)

5. The first ever show featured a sketch involving cast members in a delivery ward wondering whether a new child would be a worker, drone, or queen—of what type of creature?

6. *Saturday Night Live*'s audience increased by around a million viewers when Steve Martin made guest appearances on it, but in which year did he first appear?

7. Which fellow cast member did Chevy Chase get into a fist fight with, just moments before the show went on air in a 1978 episode?

SNL Early Days

ANSWERS

1 What was *Saturday Night Live*'s original title, used from its launch in 1975 through until 1977?

NBC's Saturday Night

The intention had been to call the show Saturday Night Live *from the start, but there was an existing ABC show called* Saturday Night Live with Howard Cosell. *Eventually NBC bought the rights to the name, and the show has used the* SNL *name ever since—apart for season six, in 1980, when it was also known as* Saturday Night Live '80.

2 Which characters, played by John Belushi and Dan Ackroyd, made their debut on the episode of January 17, 1976?

The Blues Brothers

3 Which comedian was the host of the launch episode of *Saturday Night Live*?

George Carlin

4 Unjumble the letters below to reveal one of the seven original *Saturday Night Live* cast members, known for performing the characters of Emily Litella and Roseanne Roseannadanna:

DEAR DARLING (5, 6)

Gilda Radner

5 The first ever show featured a sketch involving cast members in a delivery ward wondering whether a new child would be a worker, drone, or queen—of what type of creature?

Killer bees

6 *Saturday Night Live*'s audience increased by around a million viewers when Steve Martin made guest appearances on it, but in which year did he first appear?

1976

7 Which fellow cast member did Chevy Chase get into a fist fight with, just moments before the show went on air in a 1978 episode?

Bill Murray

1. During which 1970 NFL match was the head coach of one of the teams wired up with a microphone for the first time in the event's history, to record his in-match reactions?

2. Which two boxers fought in "The Rumble in the Jungle", broadcast live in 1974 to what was then the world's largest live-television audience?

3. Which Canadian city hosted the 1976 summer Olympics, which had an audience of approximately half a billion TV viewers for its opening ceremony?

4. Which 1976 Olympic gymnast became the first in history to score a perfect 10, a score that could not be correctly displayed because the scoreboard could only display scores up to 9.99?

5. Change one letter in each word below to reveal the name of a long-running British soccer TV show which is as identifiable by its theme tune, first introduced in 1970, as it is by its title:

   CATCH IF SHE DAB

6. Which is the name popularly given to the 1973 televised tennis match between Billie Jean King and Bobby Riggs, watched by approximately 90 million people worldwide?

7. Which sporting goods manufacturer supplied the Telstar soccer balls that featured the now-iconic 32-panel design, with 12 black pentagonal and 20 white hexagonal panels, for the 1970 World Cup?

1. During which 1970 NFL match was the head coach of one of the teams wired up with a microphone for the first time in the event's history, to record his in-match reactions?

The Super Bowl

> *The microphone given to Kansas City Chiefs's coach, Hank Stram, at Super Bowl IV was kept secret at the time, with its recorded audio used for a subsequent NFL film of the event. The recording has become legendary thanks to the coach's wry comments throughout the game.*

2. Which two boxers fought in "The Rumble in the Jungle", broadcast live in 1974 to what was then the world's largest live-television audience?

George Foreman and Muhammad Ali

3. Which Canadian city hosted the 1976 summer Olympics, which had an audience of approximately half a billion TV viewers for its opening ceremony?

Montreal

4. Which 1976 Olympic gymnast became the first in history to score a perfect 10, a score that could not be correctly displayed because the scoreboard could only display scores up to 9.99?

Nadia Comăneci

5. Change one letter in each word below to reveal the name of a long-running British soccer TV show which is as identifiable by its theme tune, first introduced in 1970, as it is by its title:

CATCH IF SHE DAB

Match of the Day

6. Which is the name popularly given to the 1973 televised tennis match between Billie Jean King and Bobby Riggs, watched by approximately 90 million people worldwide?

The Battle of the Sexes

7. Which sporting goods manufacturer supplied the Telstar soccer balls that featured the now-iconic 32-panel design, with 12 black pentagonal and 20 white hexagonal panels, for the 1970 World Cup?

Adidas

1. The sitcom *Mork & Mindy* was a spin-off inspired by a single episode of which other 1970s sitcom?

2. Which show, starring Bea Arthur as Edith's cousin, was a spin-off from *All in the Family*—and later had its own spin-off, *Good Times*?

3. *Diff'rent Strokes* lead to what 1979 spin-off show, based on Drummond's former housekeeper working at an all-girls school?

4. The sitcom *Rhoda* was the first spin-off from which sitcom named after its lead actress?

5. Which Palme d'Or-winning 1970 black-comedy war movie became a successful TV show of the same name?

6. Which police procedural drama, with a title ending in a two-digit number, is set in the same fictional world as *Dragnet* and *Emergency!*?

7. In *Cannon*, Frank meets which character, a veteran private investigator who comes out of retirement, who went on to have a show named after them?

1. The sitcom *Mork & Mindy* was a spin-off inspired by a single episode of which other 1970s sitcom?

Happy Days

Mork was an alien, played by Robin Williams, who features in the episode My Favorite Orkan, *that proved to be so popular that he was given his own show. In his audition, Williams sat in an upside-down chair, prompting producer Gary Marshall to give him the part, saying he was "the only alien to audition". Syndicated repeats of* Happy Days *were later edited to provide better continuity with the spin-off.*

2. Which show, starring Bea Arthur as Edith's cousin, was a spin-off from *All in the Family*—and later had its own spin-off, *Good Times*?

Maude

3. *Diff'rent Strokes* lead to what 1979 spin-off show, based on Drummond's former housekeeper working at an all-girls school?

The Facts of Life

4. The sitcom *Rhoda* was the first spin-off from which sitcom named after its lead actress?

The Mary Tyler Moore Show

5. Which Palme d'Or-winning 1970 black-comedy war movie became a successful TV show of the same name?

M*A*S*H

6. Which police procedural drama, with a title ending in a two-digit number, is set in the same fictional world as *Dragnet* and *Emergency!*?

Adam-12

7. In *Cannon*, Frank meets which character, a veteran private investigator who comes out of retirement, who went on to have a show named after them?

Barnaby Jones—in the show Barnaby Jones

Sci-fi & Comics 2
QUESTIONS

1. What is the name of the spin-off show from *The Six Million Dollar Man* that stars Lindsay Wagner in the role of Jaime Sommers?

2. In 1970s TV, who is the fictional character of Diana Prince better known as?

3. In *The Amazing Spider-Man* TV series, what is the name of Spider-Man's reporter girlfriend?

4. Which of the following is the correct title of an animated 1977 show?

   a. *The Amazing Adventures of Batman*
   b. *The Further Adventures of Batman*
   c. *The Incredible Adventures of Batman*
   d. *The New Adventures of Batman*

5. Unjumble the letters below to reveal the name of the actor who voices the role Captain Kirk in *Star Trek: The Animated Series*:

   SLIM ALIEN WRATH (7, 7)

6. Which TV show is based around the plight of inhabitants on Moonbase Alpha, a research facility located on the Moon?

7. What was the cause of the accident which led to Steve Austin being rebuilt as the six million dollar man, in the show of the same name?

Sci-fi & Comics 2
ANSWERS

1 What is the name of the spin-off show from *The Six Million Dollar Man* that stars Lindsay Wagner in the role of Jaime Sommers?

The Bionic Woman

The show ran from 1976 to 1978 after the positive reception the character received in The Six Million Dollar Man. *Wagner went on to win an Emmy for her performance and the show was a ratings hit. In the UK it became the only science fiction show to get to number 1 in the TV ratings in the entire 20th century.*

2 In 1970s TV, who is the fictional character of Diana Prince better known as?

Wonder Woman

3 In *The Amazing Spider-Man* TV series, what is the name of Spider-Man's reporter girlfriend?

Julie Masters

4 Which of the following is the correct title of an animated 1977 show?

a. *The Amazing Adventures of Batman*
b. *The Further Adventures of Batman*
c. *The Incredible Adventures of Batman*
d. *The New Adventures of Batman*

d. The New Adventures of Batman

5 Unjumble the letters below to reveal the name of the actor who voices the role of Captain Kirk in *Star Trek: The Animated Series:*

SLIM ALIEN WRATH (7, 7)

William Shatner

6 Which TV show is based around the plight of inhabitants on Moonbase Alpha, a research facility located on the Moon?

Space: 1999

7 What was the cause of the accident which led to Steve Austin being rebuilt as the six million dollar man, in the show of the same name?

NASA test flight crash

1. Which crime drama, which ran for most of the 1970s, featured a detective with the catchphrase, "Just one more thing"?

2. In the procedural drama series, *Hawaii Five-O*, what does the "Five-O" of the title refer to?

3. *Cannon* follows the adventures of detective Frank Cannon, who is portrayed as a veteran of which war?

4. In the series of the same name, what was unusual about Quincy M.E.'s home residence?

5. In *Kojak*, what type of candy is Lieutenant Theo Kojak most associated with?

6. How many seconds elapsed after a mission tape had been heard before it self-destructed, in most episodes of *Mission: Impossible*?

7. Crime drama *Ironside* revolves around Chief Ironside, who has been forced to retire from the San Francisco Police Department for what reason?

1. Which crime drama, which ran for most of the 1970s, featured a detective with the catchphrase, "Just one more thing"?

Columbo

The show was unusual for starting by showing the crime that would later be investigated by Columbo, including the guilty party or parties. The program therefore lacked the usual "whodunit" element of such shows, and instead focused on how the perpetrator would eventually be discovered and exposed by Columbo.

2. In the procedural drama series, *Hawaii Five-O*, what does the "Five-O" of the title refer to?

Hawaii being the 50th state, although "five-O" is now general slang for "the police"

3. *Cannon* follows the adventures of detective Frank Cannon, who is portrayed as a veteran of which war?

Korean War

4. In the series of the same name, what was unusual about Quincy M.E.'s home residence?

He lived on a sailing boat moored in Marina Del Rey, California

5. In *Kojak*, what type of candy is Lieutenant Theo Kojak most associated with?

Lollipops—which the character used as a cigarette substitute

6. How many seconds elapsed after a mission tape had been heard before it self-destructed, in most episodes of *Mission: Impossible*?

Five seconds

7. Crime drama *Ironside* revolves around Chief Ironside, who has been forced to retire from the San Francisco Police Department for what reason?

He had been hit by a sniper bullet, confining him to a wheelchair

Pot Luck 2
QUESTIONS

1 What are the first names of the two streetwise cops that feature in the title of *Starsky & Hutch*?

2 Name all six members of *Monty Python's Flying Circus*.

3 What is the nickname of the greaser played by Henry Winkler in *Happy Days*, with the nickname based on the character's surname?

4 What do the letters in *M*A*S*H* stand for, as used in the title of the war-based comedy-drama series which first aired in 1972?

5 John Forsythe played the role of Charlie in *Charlie's Angels* but was never credited. Why?

6 Rearrange the letters below to restore the name of a sitcom first broadcast in 1975, following the adventures of a New York family as they move from Queens to Manhattan:

JETS OF FRESHEN (3, 10)

7 Actress Vivian Vance was well-known to US viewers as Ethel in the 1950s show, *I Love Lucy*, but which 1978 TV program saw her final on-screen appearance?

1 What are the first names of the two streetwise cops that feature in the title of *Starsky & Hutch*?

David and Kenneth

Their full names are David Michael Starsky and Kenneth Richard Hutchinson, played on-screen by Paul Michael Glaser and David Soul, respectively. The US show was also popular in the UK, although numerous sequences were heavily cut by the BBC after being considered too graphic for British audiences—and the episode The Fix was not shown at all.

2 Name all six members of *Monty Python's Flying Circus*.

John Cleese, Graham Chapman, Terry Jones, Michael Palin, Eric Idol, and Terry Gilliam

3 What is the nickname of the greaser played by Henry Winkler in *Happy Days*, with the nickname based on the character's surname?

Fonzie

4 What do the letters in *M*A*S*H* stand for, as used in the title of the war-based comedy-drama series which first aired in 1972?

Mobile Army Surgical Hospital

5 John Forsythe played the role of Charlie in *Charlie's Angels* but was never credited. Why?

He never appeared on-screen, with a double used for scenes of his back—which the actor also thought would lend mystery to the role

6 Rearrange the letters below to restore the name of a sitcom first broadcast in 1975, following the adventures of a New York family as they move from Queens to Manhattan:

JETS OF FRESHEN (3, 10)

The Jeffersons

7 Actress Vivian Vance was well-known to US viewers as Ethel in the 1950s show, *I Love Lucy*, but which 1978 TV program saw her final on-screen appearance?

Sam—in episode six of season one

Remade in the US

1 What modified name was given to the US remake of British sitcom, *Steptoe and Son*, when it aired on NBC from 1972 until 1977?

2 *Beane's of Boston* never progressed beyond a pilot episode, but it would have been a US version of which UK sitcom set in a department store's clothing department?

3 Which beloved UK sitcom was unsuccessfully remade as *Snavely* for a pilot episode in the US in 1978, with the show now based around a highway motel?

4 *The Rear Guard*, written by Jimmy Perry, David Croft, and Arthur Julian, was a 1976 ABC pilot episode based on which popular UK sitcom?

5 Change one letter in each word below to reveal the name of the UK show that inspired the hit US sitcom, *Three's Company*:

CAN ABORT TIE MOUSE

6 *All in the Family* ran for nine seasons in the 1970s on CBS, but which existing UK sitcom was it based on?

7 Dom DeLuise starred as Stanley Belmont in the US remake of *On the Buses*, broadcast on NBC under what new title?

1 What modified name was given to the US remake of British sitcom, *Steptoe and Son*, when it aired on NBC from 1972 until 1977?

Sanford and Son

> *Starring Redd Foxx and Demond Wilson, Sanford and Son was a ratings hit for all six seasons, and paved the way for other African-American sitcoms which followed. The dynamic between the central father and son remains the same in both versions of the show, in which Lamont Sanford and Albert Steptoe both dream of independence but are unable to leave due to their family ties.*

2 *Beane's of Boston* never progressed beyond a pilot episode, but it would have been a US version of which UK sitcom set in a department store's clothing department?

Are You Being Served?

3 Which beloved UK sitcom was unsuccessfully remade as *Snavely* for a pilot episode in the US in 1978, with the show now based around a highway motel?

Fawlty Towers

4 *The Rear Guard*, written by Jimmy Perry, David Croft, and Arthur Julian, was a 1976 ABC pilot episode based on which popular UK sitcom?

Dad's Army

5 Change one letter in each word below to reveal the name of the UK show that inspired the hit US sitcom, *Three's Company*:

CAN ABORT TIE MOUSE

Man About the House

6 *All in the Family* ran for nine seasons in the 1970s on CBS, but which existing UK sitcom was it based on?

Till Death Do Us Part

7 Dom DeLuise starred as Stanley Belmont in the US remake of *On the Buses*, broadcast on NBC under what new title?

Lotsa Luck

Taglines

Can you identify which TV show was advertised with each of the following taglines?

1. "Can the funniest, most opinionated nine-year-old south of Harlem find happiness as the adopted son of a suave, lily-white Park Avenue millionaire?"

2. "She's holding her baby, she just doesn't know it yet"

3. "America, you're in for a yock... Archie, you're in for a shock"

4. "Just one more thing…"

5. "Bullets bouncing off her bracelets!"

6. "Being Gal Friday at a television station lands beautiful Mary in hilarious jams seven days a week"

7. "The lawmen are crooks, the good guys are outlaws, and ever'body's in-laws!"

8. "A lonely quest for a shining planet known as… Earth"

9. "Mystery fans, hold onto your ghosts because here come the spookiest, most spine-tingling tales ever"

Can you identify which TV show was advertised with each of the following taglines?

1 "Can the funniest, most opinionated nine-year-old south of Harlem find happiness as the adopted son of a suave, lily-white Park Avenue millionaire?"

Diff'rent Strokes

The tagline in this case functions as a neat summary of the show's central premise, which began airing in 1978. Broadcast until 1986, the show starred Gary Coleman as the aforementioned adoptee, who was ten years old at the start of filming and went on to become one of the highest-paid adolescents on television during the show's run.

2 "She's holding her baby, she just doesn't know it yet"

All My Children

3 "America, you're in for a yock... Archie, you're in for a shock"

Sandford and Son

4 "Just one more thing…"

Columbo

5 "Bullets bouncing off her bracelets!"

Wonder Woman

6 "Being Gal Friday at a television station lands beautiful Mary in hilarious jams seven days a week"

The Mary Tyler Moore Show

7 "The lawmen are crooks, the good guys are outlaws, and ever'body's in-laws!"

The Dukes of Hazzard

8 "A lonely quest for a shining planet known as… Earth"

Battlestar Galactica

9 "Mystery fans, hold onto your ghosts because here come the spookiest, most spine-tingling tales ever"

Scooby-Doo, Where Are You!

1. Which US president resigned in 1974, announcing his intention to do so in a speech which was broadcast live from the Oval Office?

2. Which iconic musician starred in the January 1973 concert *Aloha from Hawaii via Satellite*, transmitted live to Asia and Oceania but only shown later in the US to avoid clashing with the Super Bowl?

3. Which brand was advertised with a now-famous TV commercial featuring the song *I'd Like to Teach the World to Sing (In Perfect Harmony)*, but with key words replaced with the name of the brand?

4. Which band gave their final public performance on a London rooftop in January 1970, having spent a year planning for a last televised concert which was eventually shelved?

5. Which candidate for UK Prime Minister refused to appear in televised debates in the run up to the 1979 general election, but was still the eventual winner?

6. What was the name of the text-based interactive television service launched by the BBC in 1974, whose name is a pun on the phrase "see facts"?

7. Which of Queen Elizabeth's children was married in 1973 in a ceremony broadcast live to an estimated worldwide audience of 500 million?

1 Which US president resigned in 1974, announcing his intention to do so in a speech which was broadcast live from the Oval Office?

Richard Nixon

On August 8th, 1974, Nixon felt compelled to resign after his involvement in the Watergate scandal became widely known, becoming effective the next day. He was later given a full and unconditional pardon by incoming president Gerald Ford.

2 Which iconic musician starred in the January 1973 concert *Aloha from Hawaii via Satellite*, transmitted live to Asia and Oceania but only shown later in the US to avoid clashing with the Super Bowl?

Elvis Presley

3 Which brand was advertised with a now-famous TV commercial featuring the song *I'd Like to Teach the World to Sing (In Perfect Harmony)*, but with key words replaced with the name of the brand?

Coca-Cola

4 Which band gave their final public performance on a London rooftop in January 1970, having spent a year planning for a last televised concert which was eventually shelved?

The Beatles

5 Which candidate for UK Prime Minister refused to appear in televised debates in the run up to the 1979 general election, but was still the eventual winner?

Margaret Thatcher

6 What was the name of the text-based interactive television service launched by the BBC in 1974, whose name is a pun on the phrase "see facts"?

Ceefax

7 Which of Queen Elizabeth's children was married in 1973 in a ceremony broadcast live to an estimated worldwide audience of 500 million?

Princess Anne

1. How many episodes of the famous John Cleese sitcom, *Fawlty Towers*, were made in total?

2. In *The Good Life*, what is the name of the Goods' snobbish neighbor, played by Penelope Keith?

3. What is the name of the prison in the Ronnie Barker sitcom, *Porridge*, which ran from 1974 to 1977?

4. Change one letter in each word below to reveal the name of the British comedy which has the catchphrase, "I'm free!":

   APE YOB BLING NERVED?

5. Which composer wrote the theme tunes for many classic British sitcoms of the 1970s, including *The Fall and Rise of Reginald Perrin*, *Are You Being Served?*, *Some Mothers Do 'Ave 'Em* and *Last of the Summer Wine*?

6. Who is Frank Spencer, played by future musical star Michael Crawford, married to in *Some Mothers Do 'Ave 'Em*?

7. What is the name of Ronnie Barker's character in *Open All Hours*, the owner of a small grocer's shop?

1. How many episodes of the famous John Cleese sitcom, *Fawlty Towers*, were made in total?

Twelve

Although Cleese is most associated with the show, it was co-written with his then wife, Connie Booth, who played Polly in the series. Despite its huge success, with it often being ranked as the best British show of all time, only two series each of six episodes were ever made. Inspired by the way that Fawlty Towers stopped while still successful, Ricky Gervais refused to make more than two series of (British) The Office, or Extras.

2. In *The Good Life*, what is the name of the Goods' snobbish neighbor, played by Penelope Keith?

Margo Leadbetter (née Sturgess)

3. What is the name of the prison in the Ronnie Barker sitcom, *Porridge*, which ran from 1974 to 1977?

H.M.P. Slade

4. Change one letter in each word below to reveal the name of the British comedy which has the catchphrase, "I'm free!":

APE YOB BLING NERVED?

Are You Being Served?

5. Which composer wrote the theme tunes for many classic British sitcoms of the 1970s, including *The Fall and Rise of Reginald Perrin*, *Are You Being Served?*, *Some Mothers Do 'Ave 'Em* and *Last of the Summer Wine*?

Ronnie Hazlehurst

6. Who is Frank Spencer, played by future musical star Michael Crawford, married to in *Some Mothers Do 'Ave 'Em*?

Betty Spencer

7. What is the name of Ronnie Barker's character in *Open All Hours*, the owner of a small grocer's shop?

Albert Arkwright

1. In which London suburb, more commonly known for its tennis stadiums, do *The Wombles* live?

2. What type of creature is Worzel Gummidge, played by former *Doctor Who* actor Jon Pertwee?

3. Which smartly dressed animated character, who changes costume in each episode, lives at number 52 Festive Road?

4. The eruption of which Sicilian volcano in 1971 was covered on *Blue Peter* as part of its current affairs programming?

5. Dougal, Brian, Florence, and Zebedee are all characters in which surreal stop-motion show, based on a French-language original?

6. In *The Adventures of Rupert Bear*, known as *My Little Rupert* in the US, what color are the titular character's trousers?

7. What two colors are the stripes on the eponymous cat Bagpuss, whose vivid appearance was the result of a manufacturing error?

1 In which London suburb, more commonly known for its tennis stadiums, do *The Wombles* live?

Wimbledon

> They live on Wimbledon Common, a large grassy expanse not far from the courts on which the famous tennis tournament is played out. Based on a book series of the same name, the stop-motion TV show's title derives from the original author's daughter's mispronunciation of the park's name as "Wombledon Common".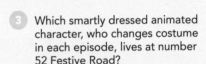

2 What type of creature is Worzel Gummidge, played by former *Doctor Who* actor Jon Pertwee?

Scarecrow

3 Which smartly dressed animated character, who changes costume in each episode, lives at number 52 Festive Road?

Mr. Benn

4 The eruption of which Sicilian volcano in 1971 was covered on *Blue Peter* as part of its current affairs programming?

Mount Etna

5 Dougal, Brian, Florence, and Zebedee are all characters in which surreal stop-motion show, based on a French-language original?

The Magic Roundabout

6 In *The Adventures of Rupert Bear*, known as *My Little Rupert* in the US, what color are the titular character's trousers?

Yellow

7 What two colors are the stripes on the eponymous cat Bagpuss, whose vivid appearance was the result of a manufacturing error?

Pink and white—or pink and cream

1 How many Brady children appear on the split-screen title card used at the opening of *The Brady Bunch*?

2 Which actor, whose movies include *Matilda* and *Romancing the Stone*, plays the role of the dispatcher in *Taxi*?

3 What is the three-letter name of the fictional Minneapolis TV station which employs Mary Tyler Moore, in the eponymous series that ran from 1970 until 1977?

4 What is the name of the Brady family dog, named after a different, striped animal?

5 What is the profession of the Chicago-based title character in *The Bob Newhart Show*, first broadcast in 1972?

6 What is the title of the sitcom starring Gary Coleman and Todd Bridges as a pair of brothers, known for its "very special episodes" dealing with controversial social issues?

7 Delete one letter from each pair below to reveal the name of a sitcom starring Robert Guillaume in the titular role, which was a spin-off of *Soap*?

TB AE NX IS OA PN

1 How many Brady children appear on the split-screen title card used at the opening of *The Brady Bunch*?

Six

> *The title sequence became an iconic TV show introduction, with headshots of all eight Brady family members—plus their housekeeper—seemingly interacting with one another across the screen. To find out during initial casting whether the child actors were able to concentrate, the producer placed toys on the desk in front of him to see how easily distracted they were.*

2 Which actor, whose movies include *Matilda* and *Romancing the Stone*, plays the role of the dispatcher in *Taxi*?

Danny DeVito

3 What is the three-letter name of the fictional Minneapolis TV station which employs Mary Tyler Moore, in the eponymous series that ran from 1970 until 1977?

WJM

4 What is the name of the Brady family dog, named after a different, striped animal?

Tiger

5 What is the profession of the Chicago-based title character in *The Bob Newhart Show*, first broadcast in 1972?

Psychologist

6 What is the title of the sitcom starring Gary Coleman and Todd Bridges as a pair of brothers, known for its "very special episodes" dealing with controversial social issues?

Diff'rent Strokes

7 Delete one letter from each pair below to reveal the name of a sitcom starring Robert Guillaume in the titular role, which was a spin-off of *Soap*?

TB AE NX IS OA PN

Benson

1. Which actor, known for his role in the movie *Grease*, played Vinnie Barbarino in the sitcom *Welcome Back, Kotter*?

2. Which late-night comedy featuring Billy Crystal opens with the announcement, "This is the story of two sisters: Jessica Tate and Mary Campbell"?

3. Change one letter in each word below to reveal the name of a children's adventure series, first broadcast in 1974, about a family who were forced to coexist with dinosaurs in an alternate universe:

   LANE ON THY MOST

4. Which comedy drama, running from 1977 for five seasons, was based on the real-life story of Tom Braden and his multiple children?

5. What extraterrestrial phrase is used by Robin Williams's character in *Mork & Mindy* to both greet others and to say farewell?

6. In *Laverne & Shirley*, what is the name of the fictional brewery that employs the titular characters?

7. In which 1970s crime drama, named after its protagonist, did the phrase "Who loves ya, baby?" frequently feature?

1. Which actor, known for his role in the movie *Grease*, played Vinnie Barbarino in the sitcom *Welcome Back, Kotter*?

John Travolta

This high-school sitcom is set in a remedial class whose members are known as the "Sweathogs", with Travolta playing an Italian-American student who occasionally breaks into song, deploying rhyming put-downs to cement his status as the group's leader. The original title of the show was due to be just Kotter, *but it was changed so that the composer of the theme tune could find more words to rhyme with it.*

2. Which late-night comedy featuring Billy Crystal opens with the announcement, "This is the story of two sisters: Jessica Tate and Mary Campbell"?

Soap

3. Change one letter in each word below to reveal the name of a children's adventure series, first broadcast in 1974, about a family who were forced to coexist with dinosaurs in an alternate universe:

LANE ON THY MOST

Land of the Lost

4. Which comedy drama, running from 1977 for five seasons, was based on the real-life story of Tom Braden and his multiple children?

Eight is Enough

5. What extraterrestrial phrase is used by Robin Williams's character in *Mork & Mindy* to both greet others and to say farewell?

Nanu nanu

6. In *Laverne & Shirley*, what is the name of the fictional brewery that employs the titular characters?

Shotz Brewery

7. In which 1970s crime drama, named after its protagonist, did the phrase "Who loves ya, baby?" frequently feature?

Kojak

1. Which US sports channel launched in 1979, opening with what would later become known as its flagship show, *SportsCenter*?

2. Which British punk band in 1976 generated huge controversy after swearing repeatedly live on air on the *Today* show?

3. Which sport enjoyed a huge increase in popularity with UK television viewers in the 1970s after the introduction of color broadcasting, which made it much easier to keep track of the different balls?

4. HBO became the first US network to transmit via satellite, in 1975, but what do the initials "H", "B", and "O" in its name stand for?

5. The Pinwheel Channel changed its title in 1979 to what one-word name, an historical nickname given to cinemas which charged five cents for admission?

6. When television was finally made available nationwide in South Africa, in 1976, what two languages were used for programming?

7. Which long-running US sports show, dedicated to the broadcast of NFL games, made its debut in 1970 on ABC?

1 Which US sports channel launched in 1979, opening with what would later become known as its flagship show, *SportsCenter*?

ESPN

Short for Entertainment and Sports Programming Network, ESPN was first broadcast to just over a million US subscribers in 1979. Despite fears that the sport TV channel would not take off with audiences at home, ESPN gained early popularity the following year by broadcasting the NFL draft for the first time.

2 Which British punk band in 1976 generated huge controversy after swearing repeatedly live on air on the *Today* show?

Sex Pistols

3 Which sport enjoyed a huge increase in popularity with UK television viewers in the 1970s after the introduction of color broadcasting, which made it much easier to keep track of the different balls?

Snooker

4 HBO became the first US network to transmit via satellite, in 1975, but what do the initials "H", "B", and "O" in its name stand for?

Home Box Office

5 The Pinwheel Channel changed its title in 1979 to what one-word name, an historical nickname given to cinemas which charged five cents for admission?

Nickelodeon

6 When television was finally made available nationwide in South Africa, in 1976, what two languages were used for programming?

English and Afrikaans

7 Which long-running US sports show, dedicated to the broadcast of NFL games, made its debut in 1970 on ABC?

Monday Night Football

Sci-fi & Comics 3

1. Terry Nation, creator of the daleks for *Doctor Who*, was also the creator of which 1978 BBC TV series that contains a single-digit number in its title?

2. The theme song to which TV show features the lyrics, "Make a hawk a dove; Stop a war with love"?

3. In *The New Adventures of Batman*, what is the name of Batman's top-hatted and monocled enemy?

4. Change one letter in each word below to reveal the title character's catchphrase in *The Incredible Hulk*:

   YOB COULDN'T LIVE WE THEN I'D UNGRY

5. What was the title of the 1970 to 1972 show which featured the Department for the Observation and Measurement of Scientific Work?

6. In the 1978 animated series, *The New Fantastic Four*, what is the character of Ben Grimm better known as?

7. What was the name of the title character's robot companion, in *Buck Rogers in the 25th Century*?

1 Terry Nation, creator of the daleks for *Doctor Who*, was also the creator of which 1978 BBC TV series that contains a single-digit number in its title?

Blake's 7

The lead actors in both Blake's 7 *and* Doctor Who *wanted to do a crossover, in which the daleks would invade at the end of the second season, but this was refused by the producers of both series. One unintended crossover that did take place, however, was that the main console of a ship appearing in the series was formed from the giant laser-gun prop used in the James Bond movie,* The Man with the Golden Gun.

2 The theme song to which TV show features the lyrics, "Make a hawk a dove; Stop a war with love"?

Wonder Woman

3 In *The New Adventures of Batman*, what is the name of Batman's top-hatted and monocled enemy?

The Penguin

4 Change one letter in each word below to reveal the title character's catchphrase in *The Incredible Hulk*:

YOB COULDN'T LIVE WE THEN I'D UNGRY

You wouldn't like me when I'm angry

5 What was the title of the 1970 to 1972 show which featured the Department for the Observation and Measurement of Scientific Work?

Doomwatch

6 In the 1978 animated series, *The New Fantastic Four*, what is the character of Ben Grimm better known as?

The Thing

7 What was the name of the title character's robot companion, in *Buck Rogers in the 25th Century*?

Twiki

MUSIC

The 70s said "see you on the flip side" to rock and roll and began to boogie down to the max to the groovy disco beats. Flairs were in, collars were huge, and everybody had a severe case of Saturday Night Fever. Funk, soul, rock and reggae were off the hook, while punk rock slammed into the scene in the second half of the decade.

Have you got The Knack for 70s music trivia? Well, then get The Gang together, bring the Kool, put your Talking Heads together and find out, One Way or Another, who's got what it takes to nail this round.

Singer-Songwriters 1
QUESTIONS

1 What is the title of the 1970 single, written by George Harrison and Bob Dylan and featuring Eric Clapton on electric guitar, which was the first track on Harrison's initial post-Beatles solo album?

2 First released on her album *Ladies of the Canyon*, which song by Joni Mitchell opens with the lyric "They paved paradise and put up a parking lot"?

3 Which Carly Simon song, first released in 1972, begins with the lyric "You walked into the party like you were walking onto a yacht"?

4 Which Simon & Garfunkel track, sharing its name with the Catholic patron saint of music, has a rhythm that was inspired by the reverb created on a tape recorder?

5 Which album, named with the initials of its recording artist, features the track *Your Smiling Face*, written during the artist's marriage to Carly Simon?

6 Rearrange the letters below to reveal the title of a 1972 single by Bill Withers, which was later covered by Club Nouveau in 1987:

NONE LAME (4, 2, 2)

7 Which track on Carole King's 1971 album, *Tapestry*, had previously been a hit for Aretha Franklin in 1967 despite the tune being written by King, and was later covered by Rod Stewart, Bonnie Tyler, Mary J. Blige, and Celine Dion?

Singer-Songwriters 1

ANSWERS

1 What is the title of the 1970 single, written by George Harrison and Bob Dylan and featuring Eric Clapton on electric guitar, which was the first track on Harrison's initial post-Beatles solo album?

I'd Have You Anytime

Harrison had already released the solo albums Wonderwall Music *and* Electronic Sound *while the Beatles were still together, having been frustrated that his musical contributions were not, he felt, given sufficient acknowledgment by Paul McCartney and Ringo Starr, the group's most prolific songwriters.*

2 First released on her album *Ladies of the Canyon*, which song by Joni Mitchell opens with the lyric "They paved paradise and put up a parking lot"?

Big Yellow Taxi

3 Which Carly Simon song, first released in 1972, begins with the lyric "You walked into the party like you were walking onto a yacht"?

You're So Vain

4 Which Simon & Garfunkel track, sharing its name with the Catholic patron saint of music, has a rhythm that was inspired by the reverb created on a tape recorder?

Cecilia

5 Which album, named with the initials of its recording artist, features the track *Your Smiling Face*, written during the artist's marriage to Carly Simon?

JT—named after James Taylor

6 Rearrange the letters below to reveal the title of a 1972 single by Bill Withers, which was later covered by Club Nouveau in 1987:

NONE LAME (4, 2, 2)

Lean On Me

7 Which track on Carole King's 1971 album, *Tapestry*, had previously been a hit for Aretha Franklin in 1967 despite the tune being written by King, and was later covered by Rod Stewart, Bonnie Tyler, Mary J. Blige, and Celine Dion?

(You Make Me Feel Like) A Natural Woman

Complete the Lyrics 1
QUESTIONS

Can you fill in the missing word in each lyric below?

1 Simon & Garfunkel, *Bridge Over Troubled Water*:

"Oh, when times get rough
And _____ just can't be found"

2 Jackson 5, *I'll Be There*:

"You and I must make a pact
We must bring _____ back"

3 Billy Paul, *Me and Mrs. Jones*:

"We meet every day at the same _____"

4 The Four Seasons, *December, 1963 (Oh, What a Night)*:

"But I was never gonna be the same,
What a _____, what a night"

5 Carpenters, *(They Long to Be) Close to You*:

"On the day that you were born
The _____ got together"

6 The Emotions, *Best of My Love*:

"Doesn't take much to make me happy
And make me smile with _____"

7 Elton John, *Crocodile Rock*:

"I remember when rock was young
Me and _____ had so much fun"

Complete the Lyrics 1

ANSWERS

Can you fill in the missing word in each lyric below?

1 Simon & Garfunkel, *Bridge Over Troubled Water*:

"Oh, when times get rough
And _____ just can't be found"

Friends

> Bridge Over Troubled Water, *from their album of the same name, is perhaps the most famous song by Simon & Garfunkel. Subsequently covered by a range of music legends, including Aretha Franklin and Elvis Presley, the song was written by Paul Simon—who later expressed regret about encouraging his bandmate to sing the lead vocals, instead of singing them himself.*

2 Jackson 5, *I'll Be There*:

"You and I must make a pact
We must bring _____ back"

Salvation

3 Billy Paul, *Me and Mrs. Jones*:

"We meet every day at the same _____"

Cafe

4 The Four Seasons, *December, 1963 (Oh, What a Night)*:

"But I was never gonna be the same,
What a _____, what a night"

Lady

5 Carpenters, *(They Long to Be) Close to You*:

"On the day that you were born
The _____ got together"

Angels

6 The Emotions, *Best of My Love*:

"Doesn't take much to make me happy
And make me smile with _____"

Glee

7 Elton John, *Crocodile Rock*:

"I remember when rock was young
Me and _____ had so much fun"

Susie

Motown
QUESTIONS

1 Change one letter in each word below to reveal the title of Marvin Gaye's thirteenth studio album, whose title track reached number one on the Billboard Hot 100:

LEGS GUT IT OF

2 What is the title of the biographical drama film produced by Motown Productions in 1972, starring Diana Ross as Billie Holiday?

3 Which song, originally released by the Marvelettes in 1961 as Motown's first number-one single, was later a 1975 hit for The Carpenters?

4 *Easy* was a top-ten hit in both the US and UK for which band, whose name had been chosen by opening a dictionary and picking out a word at random?

5 Which former member of The Miracles released *Cruisin'* in 1979, which became a number-one hit in New Zealand after peaking at number four in the US chart?

6 Which singer's version of *War* became a number-one hit in the US in 1970, in the same year that The Temptations also recorded a version?

7 Which 1970 single by Stevie Wonder, taken from an album with a similar name, opens with the line "Like a fool I went and stayed too long"?

Motown
ANSWERS

1 Change one letter in each word below to reveal the title of Marvin Gaye's thirteenth studio album, whose title track reached number one on the Billboard Hot 100:

LEGS GUT IT OF

Let's Get It On

The title track went on to become one of Gaye's best-known songs, and the suggestive lyrics marked a liberation of previous constraints in the music industry at the time. The album was Gaye's best-selling record during his time with Motown, even surpassing his earlier success with What's Going On.

2 What is the title of the biographical drama film produced by Motown Productions in 1972, starring Diana Ross as Billie Holiday?

Lady Sings the Blues

3 Which song, originally released by the Marvelettes in 1961 as Motown's first number-one single, was later a 1975 hit for The Carpenters?

Please Mr. Postman

4 *Easy* was a top-ten hit in both the US and UK for which band, whose name had been chosen by opening a dictionary and picking out a word at random?

Commodores

5 Which former member of The Miracles released *Cruisin'* in 1979, which became a number-one hit in New Zealand after peaking at number four in the US chart?

Smokey Robinson

6 Which singer's version of *War* became a number-one hit in the US in 1970, in the same year that The Temptations also recorded a version?

Edwin Starr

7 Which 1970 single by Stevie Wonder, taken from an album with a similar name, opens with the line "Like a fool I went and stayed too long"?

Signed, Sealed, Delivered I'm Yours

Disco 1
QUESTIONS

1 Which 1977 album, created for a film of the same name, won Album of the Year at the Grammys, and features several Bee Gees songs?

2 *It's My House* was a hit for which singer who had previously been the lead singer of the Supremes?

3 Written as a lyrical tribute to their home city of Stockholm, which band released *Summer Night City* in 1978?

4 Which girl group released the single *Lost in Music* from their 1979 album, *We Are Family*?

5 Which 1978 track by Gloria Gaynor won the only Grammy ever awarded for Best Disco Recording?

6 McFadden & Whitehead recorded and released a 1979 song, whose lyrics and title refer to their royalty struggles with a record company. What was its name?

7 Using a mix of both French and English vocabulary, which 1987 song by Chic features the band's name in its chorus lyrics?

Disco 1
ANSWERS

1 Which 1977 album, created for a film of the same name, won Album of the Year at the Grammys, and features several Bee Gees songs?

Saturday Night Fever

Featuring the Bee Gees tracks Night Fever, Stayin' Alive *and* More Than a Woman, *the album went on to become one of the best-selling movie soundtracks of all time. John Travolta, the film's star, later revealed that the involvement of the Bee Gees didn't commence until after shooting, and that he was dancing to different tracks during filming.*

2 *It's My House* was a hit for which singer who had previously been the lead singer of the Supremes?

Diana Ross

3 Written as a lyrical tribute to their home city of Stockholm, which band released *Summer Night City* in 1978?

ABBA

4 Which girl group released the single *Lost in Music* from their 1979 album, *We Are Family*?

Sister Sledge

5 Which 1978 track by Gloria Gaynor won the only Grammy ever awarded for Best Disco Recording?

I Will Survive

6 McFadden & Whitehead recorded and released a 1979 song, whose lyrics and title refer to their royalty struggles with a record company. What was its name?

Ain't No Stoppin' Us Now

7 Using a mix of both French and English vocabulary, which 1987 song by Chic features the band's name in its chorus lyrics?

Le Freak

Legends 1
QUESTIONS

1 Which 1976 song by Rod Stewart topped the US Billboard Top 100 for eight consecutive weeks, beating the previous record holder *Hey Jude*?

2 How old was Kate Bush when she topped the UK singles charts with the track *Wuthering Heights*?

a. 17
b. 19
c. 21
d. 23

3 Which 1979 song, by new-wave band Blondie, opens with the lyrics "Once I had a love and it was a gas"?

4 Who released *The Ballad of Billy the Kid* in 1974 from his album *Piano Man*, with lyrics documenting the life of an outlaw with whom he shares a first name?

5 What was the title of Elton John's duet with Kiki Dee that became his first number one in the UK, and the first to top both the UK and US charts?

6 Which single, taken from their album *Rumours*, is the only track by Fleetwood Mac to have reached the top of the Billboard Hot 100?

7 *Don't Stop 'Til You Get Enough* and *Rock with You* were the first and second singles released from which 1979 album by Michael Jackson?

1 Which 1976 song by Rod Stewart topped the US Billboard Top 100 for eight consecutive weeks, beating the previous record holder *Hey Jude*?

Tonight's the Night (Gonna Be Alright)

> *Reportedly inspired by the song* Today's the Day, *which had been a success for the US band America, Rod Stewart's song initially caused controversy thanks to its suggestive lyrics. It nevertheless became Stewart's longest-running number one in the US, although the song only reached number five in the UK charts.*

2 How old was Kate Bush when she topped the UK singles charts with the track *Wuthering Heights*?

a. 17
b. 19
c. 21
d. 23

b. 19

3 Which 1979 song, by new-wave band Blondie, opens with the lyrics "Once I had a love and it was a gas"?

Heart of Glass

4 Who released *The Ballad of Billy the Kid* in 1974 from his album *Piano Man*, with lyrics documenting the life of an outlaw with whom he shares a first name?

Billy Joel

5 What was the title of Elton John's duet with Kiki Dee that became his first number one in the UK, and the first to top both the UK and US charts?

Don't Go Breaking My Heart

6 Which single, taken from their album *Rumours*, is the only track by Fleetwood Mac to have reached the top of the Billboard Hot 100?

Dreams

7 *Don't Stop 'Til You Get Enough* and *Rock with You* were the first and second singles released from which 1979 album by Michael Jackson?

Off the Wall

Number Ones

QUESTIONS

1 *Killing Me Softly with His Song*, which spent five weeks at number one on the Billboard Hot 100, was a hit for which "quiet storm" singer?

2 Which song, co-written by Burt Bacharach and featured in the film *Butch Cassidy and the Sundance Kid*, became the first Billboard Hot 100 number-one song of the 1970s?

3 Which Bee Gees song spent eight consecutive weeks at the top of the Billboard Top 100 in the 1970s, earning it the decade's joint second-place record for most consecutive weeks at the top?

4 Change one letter in each word below to reveal the title of a Johnny Nash song, later re-recorded for the 1993 film *Cool Runnings*:

A CAR SET CLEANLY NEW

5 *A Horse with No Name* was a hit for which then-UK-based band, whose name was chosen as a tribute to their heritage?

6 What is the name of the Don McLean song which makes repeated reference to "the day the music died"?

7 Which Melanie song, released in 1971, features the lyric "I've got a brand-new pair of roller skates"?

Number Ones

ANSWERS

1 *Killing Me Softly with His Song*, which spent five weeks at number one on the Billboard Hot 100, was a hit for which "quiet storm" singer?

Roberta Flack

Prior to its 1972 recording, the singer had performed the song live while supporting Marvin Gaye, after he had encouraged her to add an additional encore song. After its subsequent single release, the track went on to win Record of the Year at the Grammys, along with Best Female Pop Vocal Performance.

2 Which song, co-written by Burt Bacharach and featured in the film *Butch Cassidy and the Sundance Kid*, became the first Billboard Hot 100 number-one song of the 1970s?

Raindrops Keep Fallin' on My Head

3 Which Bee Gees song spent eight consecutive weeks at the top of the Billboard Top 100 in the 1970s, earning it the decade's joint second-place record for most consecutive weeks at the top?

Night Fever

4 Change one letter in each word below to reveal the title of a Johnny Nash song, later re-recorded for the 1993 film *Cool Runnings*:

A CAR SET CLEANLY NEW

I Can See Clearly Now

5 *A Horse with No Name* was a hit for which then-UK-based band, whose name was chosen as a tribute to their heritage?

America

6 What is the name of the Don McLean song which makes repeated reference to "the day the music died"?

American Pie

7 Which Melanie song, released in 1971, features the lyric "I've got a brand-new pair of roller skates"?

Brand New Key

Rock Bands 1
QUESTIONS

1 Who was Led Zeppelin's lead vocalist, right through from the band's original inception in 1968 to its eventual breakup in 1980?

2 Which Birmingham-based band featured Ozzy Osbourne as its lead singer, who took the nickname "The Prince of Darkness"?

3 Which 1972 Deep Purple song, released as a single in 1973, was inspired by the fire which destroyed the Swiss building the band had been due to record in?

4 Which 1977 album by Pink Floyd features London's Battersea Power Station as part of its cover art?

5 Which was the fifth studio album released by The Doors, featuring the surname of its lead singer in its title?

6 Roger Daltrey, Pete Townshend, and Keith Moon are all members of which band, who recorded and released the album *Live at Leeds* in 1970?

7 Rearrange the letters below to reveal the name of the only single by the Eagles to enter the UK top 10:

NOT HEROICAL FAIL (5, 10)

Rock Bands 1
ANSWERS

1 Who was Led Zeppelin's lead vocalist, right through from the band's original inception in 1968 to its eventual breakup in 1980?

Robert Plant

One of the best-known frontmen in rock history, Plant created the band Led Zeppelin with guitarist Jimmy Page in the late 1960s, although they were originally known as the New Yardbirds. After the band's breakup, Plant continued to collaborate with Page, and a much-hyped reunion was a feature of the 1985 Live Aid concert.

2 Which Birmingham-based band featured Ozzy Osbourne as its lead singer, who took the nickname "The Prince of Darkness"?

Black Sabbath

3 Which 1972 Deep Purple song, released as a single in 1973, was inspired by the fire which destroyed the Swiss building the band had been due to record in?

Smoke on the Water

4 Which 1977 album by Pink Floyd features London's Battersea Power Station as part of its cover art?

Animals

5 Which was the fifth studio album released by The Doors, featuring the surname of its lead singer in its title?

Morrison Hotel

6 Roger Daltrey, Pete Townshend, and Keith Moon are all members of which band, who recorded and released the album *Live at Leeds* in 1970?

The Who

7 Rearrange the letters below to reveal the name of the only single by the Eagles to enter the UK top 10:

NOT HEROICAL FAIL (5, 10)

Hotel California

Pot Luck 1
QUESTIONS

1 Which family musical group released *One Bad Apple* in 1970, a track which had originally been written for the Jackson 5?

2 Which 1979 song by Peaches & Herb was written as a sequel to an earlier track by the same songwriters, *(We'll Be) United*?

3 Which singer released *Bad Girls* from her 1979 album of the same name, and which was nominated for a Grammy for Best Disco Recording?

4 *Family Affair* was a 1971 hit for which band, several of whose members were from the same family?

5 What is the title of the 1971 single by Three Dog Night which has the opening line "Jeremiah was a bullfrog"?

6 What is the title of the only Sammy Davis Jr. song to reach number one on the Billboard Top 100, a version of which originally appeared in the film *Willy Wonka & The Chocolate Factory*?

7 Rearrange the letters below to spell out the name of a 1971 single from Harry Nilsson, who initially mistook it for a Beatles song:

THOU YOU WIT (7, 3)

Pot Luck 1
ANSWERS

1 Which family musical group released *One Bad Apple* in 1970, a track which had originally been written for the Jackson 5?

The Osmonds

> *The song is now one of the very few tracks by the Osmonds to still receive regular airplay, in spite of their massive popularity during the 1970s. The Jackson 5 apparently passed on the track in order to record the song ABC, which went on to become one of their most successful hits.*

2 Which 1979 song by Peaches & Herb was written as a sequel to an earlier track by the same songwriters, *(We'll Be) United*?

Reunited

3 Which singer released *Bad Girls* from her 1979 album of the same name, and which was nominated for a Grammy for Best Disco Recording?

Donna Summer

4 *Family Affair* was a 1971 hit for which band, several of whose members were from the same family?

Sly and the Family Stone

5 What is the title of the 1971 single by Three Dog Night which has the opening line "Jeremiah was a bullfrog"?

Joy to the World

6 What is the title of the only Sammy Davis Jr. song to reach number one on the Billboard Top 100, a version of which originally appeared in the film *Willy Wonka & The Chocolate Factory*?

The Candy Man

7 Rearrange the letters below to spell out the name of a 1971 single from Harry Nilsson, who initially mistook it for a Beatles song:

THOU YOU WIT (7, 3)

Without You

Soul & Funk 1
QUESTIONS

1. Change one letter in each word below to restore the title of a James Brown song, written to encourage people to dance to funk music:

   SET US OFFS WHAT THINE

2. Which group, who had a 1977 hit with the single *Best of My Love*, recorded *Boogie Wonderland* along with Earth, Wind & Fire?

3. Which band released the singles *Get Down Tonight*, *Boogie Shoes*, and *That's The Way (I Like It)* in the 1970s?

4. *Ladies' Night* is a 1979 single from the album of the same name by which R&B/funk band?

5. Who is the writer and lead singer of the Commodores's 1978 single, *Three Times a Lady*?

6. Rearrange the letters below to reveal the title of a 1973 funk song, written and performed by Stevie Wonder:

   GRID-HUNG HERO (6, 6)

7. Which well-known 1974 Barry White disco track was originally written as a country song? In White's version, he replaced the word "In-between" in its title with "Everything".

Soul & Funk 1
ANSWERS

1 Change one letter in each word below to restore the title of a James Brown song, written to encourage people to dance to funk music:

SET US OFFS WHAT THINE

Get Up Offa That Thing

> *The song is one of Brown's best-known, despite only peaking at number 45 on the Billboard Hot 100. He wrote the song in response to seeing audiences sitting and listening to live funk music, instead of engaging in what he felt was the only appropriate way: getting up and dancing. Although he wrote the song, he later credited it to his wife and daughters for tax reasons.*

2 Which group, who had a 1977 hit with the single *Best of My Love*, recorded *Boogie Wonderland* along with Earth, Wind & Fire?

The Emotions

3 Which band released the singles *Get Down Tonight*, *Boogie Shoes*, and *That's The Way (I Like It)* in the 1970s?

KC and the Sunshine Band

4 *Ladies' Night* is a 1979 single from the album of the same name by which R&B/funk band?

Kool & the Gang

5 Who is the writer and lead singer of the Commodores's 1978 single, *Three Times a Lady*?

Lionel Richie

6 Rearrange the letters below to reveal the title of a 1973 funk song, written and performed by Stevie Wonder:

GRID-HUNG HERO (6, 6)

Higher Ground

7 Which well-known 1974 Barry White disco track was originally written as a country song? In White's version, he replaced the word "In-between" in its title with "Everything".

You're the First, the Last, My Everything

One-Hit Wonders 1
QUESTIONS

1 Which band released the track *My Sharona* in 1979, said to have been written in just fifteen minutes?

2 Which song, recorded by King Harvest in 1972, went on to also become a 2000 hit for the band Toploader?

3 Can you name the martial art that forms part of the title of a 1974 disco song from Carl Douglas?

4 Rearrange the letters below to reveal the title of a 1975 disco song by Van McCoy & the Soul City Symphony:

LUSH TEETH (3, 6)

5 Change one letter in each word below to reveal the name of a single by Australian singer John Paul Young:

MOVE IF ON TIE AID

6 Which group released *Afternoon Delight* in 1976, winning them Best Arrangement for Voices at the Grammys?

7 What is the name of the 1973 single by Stealers Wheel which mentions both clowns and jokers in its chorus?

One-Hit Wonders 1

ANSWERS

1 Which band released the track *My Sharona* in 1979, said to have been written in just fifteen minutes?

The Knack

The song was inspired by the lead vocalist's then-girlfriend, who also appeared on the cover art for the single holding the band's debut album. The song peaked at number one in the US, and became the overall number-one track of 1979 on the Billboard Year-End chart.

2 Which song, recorded by King Harvest in 1972, went on to also become a 2000 hit for the band Toploader?

Dancing in the Moonlight

3 Can you name the martial art that forms part of the title of a 1974 disco song from Carl Douglas?

Kung Fu—in the track *Kung Fu Fighting*

4 Rearrange the letters below to reveal the title of a 1975 disco song by Van McCoy & the Soul City Symphony:

LUSH TEETH (3, 6)

The Hustle

5 Change one letter in each word below to reveal the name of a single by Australian singer John Paul Young:

MOVE IF ON TIE AID

Love Is in the Air

6 Which group released *Afternoon Delight* in 1976, winning them Best Arrangement for Voices at the Grammys?

Starland Vocal Band

7 What is the name of the 1973 single by Stealers Wheel which mentions both clowns and jokers in its chorus?

Stuck in the Middle with You

Oscar Songs
QUESTIONS

1 Which song from *Grease*, performed by Olivia Newton-John, was nominated for an Oscar for Best Original Song?

2 What is the name of the animated Disney film whose soundtrack featured the songs *Oo-De-Lally* and the Oscar-nominated *Love*?

3 *Evergreen* won Best Original Song at the Academy Awards after being co-written by Barbra Streisand for which film?

4 Which 1973 film, whose score was nominated for an Academy Award, is based on an Andrew Lloyd Webber musical of the same name, and features the song *I Don't Know How to Love Him*?

5 Which of these films was *not* Oscar-nominated for a score composed by John Williams?

a. *Superman*
b. *Close Encounters of the Third Kind*
c. *Jaws*
d. *Earthquake*

6 Which brother-sister duo performed *Bless the Beasts and Children* for the 1971 film of the same name, a track which was nominated for an Academy Award for Best Original Song?

7 Complete the title of one of the movies nominated for Best Original Song at the 1979 Oscars by adding in the name of a fictional animal:

The Magic of ____

Oscar Songs
ANSWERS

1 Which song from *Grease*, performed by Olivia Newton-John, was nominated for an Oscar for Best Original Song?

Hopelessly Devoted to You

The song was written and added to the production after much of the filming had already taken place, having not been part of the preceding Broadway stage musical. The music was written by Newton-John's producer, who also wrote You're The One that I Want—*which later became one of the best-selling singles of all time.*

2 What is the name of the animated Disney film whose soundtrack featured the songs *Oo-De-Lally* and the Oscar-nominated *Love*?

Robin Hood

3 *Evergreen* won Best Original Song at the Academy Awards after being co-written by Barbra Streisand for which film?

A Star is Born

4 Which 1973 film, whose score was nominated for an Academy Award, is based on an Andrew Lloyd Webber musical of the same name, and features the song *I Don't Know How to Love Him*?

Jesus Christ Superstar

5 Which of these films was *not* Oscar-nominated for a score composed by John Williams?

a. *Superman*
b. *Close Encounters of the Third Kind*
c. *Jaws*
d. *Earthquake*

d. Earthquake

6 Which brother-sister duo performed *Bless the Beasts and Children* for the 1971 film of the same name, a track which was nominated for an Academy Award for Best Original Song?

The Carpenters

7 Complete the title of one of the movies nominated for Best Original Song at the 1979 Oscars by adding in the name of a fictional animal:

The Magic of _____

The Magic of Lassie

Disco 2

QUESTIONS

1 Change one letter in each word below to reveal the name of a Bee Gees song which won them a Grammy for Best Pop Vocal Performance by a Group:

HOT WEEP IF HOUR DOVE

2 In which 1976 ABBA song would you hear the lyrics "Friday night and the lights are low"?

3 Which Sister Sledge song features the lyric "One night in a disco on the outskirts of Frisco"?

4 Rearrange the letters below to reveal the title of the Chic song which went on to be used heavily in the Sugarhill Gang track, *Rapper's Delight*?

DO EGOTISM (4, 5)

5 *Daddy Cool* was a hit for which band, originally formed in West Germany, who later had a Christmas hit with *Mary's Boy Child / Oh My Lord*?

6 What is the two-word name of the album released by Diana Ross in 1979, in which the second word rhymes with one of the singer's names?

7 Which band released *Boogie Nights* in 1977 from their album *Too Hot to Handle*, a track that was later covered by KC & the Sunshine Band?

Disco 2
ANSWERS

1 Change one letter in each word below to reveal the name of a Bee Gees song which won them a Grammy for Best Pop Vocal Performance by a Group:

HOT WEEP IF HOUR DOVE

How Deep is Your Love

> *Released in 1977, the song was used in the soundtrack to the dance film* Saturday Night Fever, *starring John Travolta. The song was highly successful in the US, remaining in the top 10 of the Billboard Hot 100 for 17 weeks. The song was later covered by British boy band Take That, whose version peaked at number one in the UK.*

2 In which 1976 ABBA song would you hear the lyrics "Friday night and the lights are low"?

Dancing Queen

3 Which Sister Sledge song features the lyric "One night in a disco on the outskirts of Frisco"?

He's the Greatest Dancer

4 Rearrange the letters below to reveal the title of the Chic song which went on to be used heavily in the Sugarhill Gang track, *Rapper's Delight*?

DO EGOTISM (4, 5)

Good Times

5 *Daddy Cool* was a hit for which band, originally formed in West Germany, who later had a Christmas hit with *Mary's Boy Child / Oh My Lord*?

Boney M.

6 What is the two-word name of the album released by Diana Ross in 1979, in which the second word rhymes with one of the singer's names?

The Boss

7 Which band released *Boogie Nights* in 1977 from their album *Too Hot to Handle*, a track that was later covered by KC & the Sunshine Band?

Heatwave

Singer-Songwriters 2
QUESTIONS

1 Which album by Simon & Garfunkel became their final studio release together, and the only album they released during the 1970s?

2 Rearrange the letters below to reveal the name of Carole King's second album, which won Album of the Year at the 1972 Grammy awards:

STAR TYPE (8)

3 Who released their third studio album, *Born to Run*, in 1975, which included the artist's first worldwide single release?

4 For which James Bond film was the Carly Simon song *Nobody Does It Better* recorded?

5 The single *Fire and Rain* was released from which James Taylor album, which opens with its title track?

6 Which song was recorded separately in 1971 by both Carole King, who wrote it, and James Taylor, with Joni Mitchell featuring as a backing singer on both recordings?

7 The Bill Withers song, *Lovely Day*, is notable for its sustained note near the end, which Withers holds for how many seconds?

a. 14 seconds
b. 18 seconds
c. 22 seconds
d. 26 seconds

Singer-Songwriters 2

ANSWERS

1 Which album by Simon & Garfunkel became their final studio release together, and the only album they released during the 1970s?

Bridge Over Troubled Water

Once the best-selling album of all time, Bridge Over Troubled Water *proved to be the last studio album released by the duo, whose working relationship had broken down during the recording. It won Album of the Year at the Grammy Awards, and its title track has been covered by several artists, including Aretha Franklin and Elvis Presley.*

2 Rearrange the letters below to reveal the name of Carole King's second album, which won Album of the Year at the 1972 Grammy awards:

STAR TYPE (8)

Tapestry

3 Who released their third studio album, *Born to Run,* in 1975, which included the artist's first worldwide single release?

Bruce Springsteen

4 For which James Bond film was the Carly Simon song *Nobody Does It Better* recorded?

The Spy Who Loved Me

5 The single *Fire and Rain* was released from which James Taylor album, which opens with its title track?

Sweet Baby James

6 Which song was recorded separately in 1971 by both Carole King, who wrote it, and James Taylor, with Joni Mitchell featuring as a backing singer on both recordings?

You've Got a Friend

7 The Bill Withers song, *Lovely Day,* is notable for its sustained note near the end, which Withers holds for how many seconds?

a. 14 seconds
b. 18 seconds
c. 22 seconds
d. 26 seconds

b. 18 seconds

Legends 2

QUESTIONS

1 Which 1973 Elton John album features the tracks *Bennie and the Jets*, *Candle in the Wind*, and *Saturday Night's Alright for Fighting*?

2 Which Billy Joel song begins with the line "She can kill with a smile, she can wound with her eyes"?

3 What is the title of Kate Bush's debut album, released in 1978, which features the single *The Man with the Child in His Eyes*?

4 What is the name of Michael Jackson's first solo US number one single, which was also nominated for the Oscar for Best Original Song for its use in the one-word film of the name?

5 Reveal the name of a 1979 song by Blondie, inspired by Debbie Harry's experience of being stalked, from which all the vowels have been removed and the spacing changed:

N   WY   R   NTHR

6 What is the alliterative title of the Rod Stewart song which features the lyric "You stole my heart and that's what really hurts"?

7 Which of these tracks does *not* feature on the Fleetwood Mac album *Rumours*?

a. Don't Stop
b. Songbird
c. Albatross
d. The Chain

70s

Legends 2
ANSWERS

1. Which 1973 Elton John album features the tracks *Bennie and the Jets*, *Candle in the Wind*, and *Saturday Night's Alright for Fighting*?

   Goodbye Yellow Brick Road

   Elton John's seventh studio album is widely regarded as one of his best, and features several of his most successful songs. The track Candle in the Wind *had been written as a tribute to Hollywood legend Marilyn Monroe, but was later rerecorded in 1997 with new lyrics in memory of Diana, Princess of Wales.*

2. Which Billy Joel song begins with the line "She can kill with a smile, she can wound with her eyes"?

   She's Always a Woman

3. What is the title of Kate Bush's debut album, released in 1978, which features the single *The Man with the Child in His Eyes*?

   The Kick Inside

4. What is the name of Michael Jackson's first solo US number one single, which was also nominated for the Oscar for Best Original Song for its use in the one-word film of the name?

   Ben

5. Reveal the name of a 1979 song by Blondie, inspired by Debbie Harry's experience of being stalked, from which all the vowels have been removed and the spacing changed:

   N WY R NTHR

   One Way or Another

6. What is the alliterative title of the Rod Stewart song which features the lyric "You stole my heart and that's what really hurts"?

   Maggie May

7. Which of these tracks does *not* feature on the Fleetwood Mac album *Rumours*?

   a. Don't Stop
   b. Songbird
   c. Albatross
   d. The Chain

   c. Albatross

Rock Bands 2
QUESTIONS

1 Which member of the rock band Faces went on to become an official member of the Rolling Stones in 1976?

2 Which Australian rock band's name was taken from an abbreviation they found on the sewing machine of the sister of the two founders?

3 Which band released *God Save the Queen* in 1977, a track that was banned from BBC airplay? It was the second release from their only studio album.

4 Can you name the 1976 track by Blue Öyster Cult which allegedly inspired the Stephen King novel, *The Stand*?

5 Which band released the singles *Lady*, *Babe*, and *Come Sail Away* in the 1970s?

6 Delete one letter from each pair below to reveal the name of a song by The Rolling Stones, found on their album *Goats Head Soup*:

WA IN GT TI ER

7 At the beginning of which song by Queen can Freddie Mercury be heard playing the same piano that had been used for the recording of *Hey Jude*, before then breaking into an operatic section?

Rock Bands 2
ANSWERS

1 Which member of the rock band Faces went on to become an official member of the Rolling Stones in 1976?

Ronnie Wood

As a member of Faces, Wood frequently collaborated with lead singer Rod Stewart, who was also finding solo success at the time. Wood recorded his own solo record in 1974, entitled I've Got My Own Album to Do, *which featured input from former Beatle George Harrison, as well as future Rolling Stones bandmates Mick Jagger and Keith Richards.*

2 Which Australian rock band's name was taken from an abbreviation they found on the sewing machine of the sister of the two founders?

AC/DC

3 Which band released *God Save the Queen* in 1977, a track that was banned from BBC airplay? It was the second release from their only studio album.

The Sex Pistols

4 Can you name the 1976 track by Blue Öyster Cult which allegedly inspired the Stephen King novel, *The Stand*?

(Don't Fear) The Reaper

5 Which band released the singles *Lady*, *Babe*, and *Come Sail Away* in the 1970s?

Styx

6 Delete one letter from each pair below to reveal the name of a song by The Rolling Stones, found on their album *Goats Head Soup*:

WA IN GT TI ER

Angie

7 At the beginning of which song by Queen can Freddie Mercury be heard playing the same piano that had been used for the recording of *Hey Jude*, before then breaking into an operatic section?

Bohemian Rhapsody

Complete the Lyrics 2

QUESTIONS

Can you fill in the missing word in each lyric below?

1 Rupert Holmes, *Escape (The Pina Colada Song)*:

"I'm not much into health food
I am into _____"

2 Stevie Wonder, *Sir Duke*:

"Music is a _____ within
itself
With a language we all
understand"

3 Jim Croce, *Bad, Bad Leroy Brown*:

"Well the south side of
_____
Is the baddest part of town"

4 Wings, *Silly Love Songs*:

"You'd think that _____
would have had enough of
silly love songs"

5 Andy Gibb, *Shadow Dancing*:

"You got me looking
At that _____ in your
eyes"

6 Paul Simon, *50 Ways to Leave Your Lover*:

"You just slip out the back,
Jack
Make a new plan,
_____"

7 Gladys Knight & The Pips, *Midnight Train to Georgia*:

"He kept dreaming
Oh, that someday he'd be a
_____"

Complete the Lyrics 2

ANSWERS

Can you fill in the missing word in each lyric below?

1 Rupert Holmes, *Escape (The Pina Colada Song)*:

"I'm not much into health food
I am into _____"

Champagne

> *According to Holmes, the song's famous chorus line, "If you like pina coladas", was originally written with the name of actor Humphrey Bogart instead of the now-iconic cocktail. The tropical drink was substituted into the lyrics in spite of Holmes never having tried one, and the song went on to become the final US number one of the 1970s.*

2 Stevie Wonder, *Sir Duke*:

"Music is a _____ within itself
With a language we all understand"

World

3 Jim Croce, *Bad, Bad Leroy Brown*:

"Well the south side of _____
Is the baddest part of town"

Chicago

4 Wings, *Silly Love Songs*:

"You'd think that _____
would have had enough of silly love songs"

People

5 Andy Gibb, *Shadow Dancing*:

"You got me looking
At that _____ in your eyes"

Heaven

6 Paul Simon, *50 Ways to Leave Your Lover*:

"You just slip out the back, Jack
Make a new plan, _____"

Stan

7 Gladys Knight & The Pips, *Midnight Train to Georgia*:

"He kept dreaming
Oh, that someday he'd be a _____"

Star

End of The Beatles
QUESTIONS

1 What is the name of the twelfth and final album released by The Beatles, in 1970?

2 Delete one letter from each pair below to reveal the name of a song by John Lennon, which topped the UK charts for the first time after the singer's death:

IN SM TA GA NI NT EK

3 Which former Beatle released a self-titled album in 1973 featuring performances from Randy Newman, Vini Poncia, and all three of his former bandmates?

4 Which former Beatle recorded the song *Maybe I'm Amazed* in 1970, on the recording of which he played all of the instrument tracks?

5 What is the name of the band Paul McCartney went on to form with his wife Linda, which had a 1977 hit with the single *Mull of Kintyre*?

6 Rearrange the letters below to reveal the name of John Lennon's fourth solo album:

ME SING MAD (4, 5)

7 What is the title of the George Harrison album which features the tracks *My Sweet Lord* and *Isn't It a Pity*?

End of The Beatles

ANSWERS

1 What is the name of the twelfth and final album released by The Beatles, in 1970?

Let It Be

Get Back *was originally suggested as the name for the album, but this was eventually rejected by the band and replaced by the name of the sixth track on the record. The album's songs were recorded over a two-year period from 1968 to 1970, during which the band also released the album* Abbey Road.

2 Delete one letter from each pair below to reveal the name of a song by John Lennon, which topped the UK charts for the first time after the singer's death:

IN SM TA GA NI NT EK

Imagine

3 Which former Beatle released a self-titled album in 1973 featuring performances from Randy Newman, Vini Poncia, and all three of his former bandmates?

Ringo Starr

4 Which former Beatle recorded the song *Maybe I'm Amazed* in 1970, on the recording of which he played all of the instrument tracks?

Paul McCartney

5 What is the name of the band Paul McCartney went on to form with his wife Linda, which had a 1977 hit with the single *Mull of Kintyre*?

Wings

6 Rearrange the letters below to reveal the name of John Lennon's fourth solo album:

ME SING MAD (4, 5)

Mind Games

7 What is the title of the George Harrison album which features the tracks *My Sweet Lord* and *Isn't It a Pity*?

All Things Must Pass

Soul & Funk 2

QUESTIONS

1. What is the title of Marvin Gaye's 1971 concept album, whose socially conscious lyrics tell the imaginary story of a veteran returning from the Vietnam War?

2. Which singer released *Let's Stay Together* in 1971, a song which was later covered by Tina Turner?

3. Which musician, and former member of the Famous Flames, is often referred to as "The Godfather of Soul"?

4. The Jackson 5 had their first Billboard Top 100 hit, in January 1970, with which track?

5. Which 1976 single by Wild Cherry was the band's only number one hit on the Billboard Top 100?

6. Delete one letter from each pair below to reveal the name of an Earth, Wind & Fire song which features the lyric "ba de ya" in the chorus:

   SB OE PO GT IE NM BI HE RT

7. What is the one-word title of the song written and performed by Stevie Wonder which won two awards at the Grammys in 1974, two years after its release?

Soul & Funk 2
ANSWERS

1 What is the title of Marvin Gaye's 1971 concept album, whose socially conscious lyrics tell the imaginary story of a veteran returning from the Vietnam War?

What's Going On

Although it was the singer's eleventh studio album, it was the first on which he was named as producer. Ranked at the top spot in Rolling Stone's 2020 list of the 500 Greatest Albums of All Time, the album is considered a classic of the soul genre, with the title track alone having sold in excess of two million copies.

2 Which singer released *Let's Stay Together* in 1971, a song which was later covered by Tina Turner?

Al Green

3 Which musician, and former member of the Famous Flames, is often referred to as "The Godfather of Soul"?

James Brown

4 The Jackson 5 had their first Billboard Top 100 hit, in January 1970, with which track?

I Want You Back

5 Which 1976 single by Wild Cherry was the band's only number one hit on the Billboard Top 100?

Play That Funky Music

6 Delete one letter from each pair below to reveal the name of an Earth, Wind & Fire song which features the lyric "ba de ya" in the chorus:

SB OE PO GT IE NM BI HE RT

September

7 What is the one-word title of the song written and performed by Stevie Wonder which won two awards at the Grammys in 1974, two years after its release?

Superstition

Pot Luck 2
QUESTIONS

1. Which hugely successful song by Minnie Riperton, that opens with birds tweeting, has a melody written by the singer and her husband in order to distract their daughter Maya, whose name can be heard at the end of the original album track?

2. Which group recorded *Pick Up the Pieces* in 1974, which has no lyrics other than the occasional repetition of the song's title?

3. Delete one letter from each pair to reveal the name of Barry Manilow's first number-one single in the US:

   BM RA NK ED YS

4. On which 1972 album by Stevie Wonder do the tracks *Superstition* and *You Are the Sunshine of My Life* feature?

5. *I Am Woman* was a 1972 hit for which singer, whose debut album was titled *I Don't Know How to Love Him*?

6. Who wrote and recorded the 1974 hit *(You're) Having My Baby*, performed as a duet with Odia Coates?

7. Which song by The O'Jays mentions the countries England, China, Egypt, and Israel in its lyrics?

1 Which hugely successful song by Minnie Riperton, that opens with birds tweeting, has a melody written by the singer and her husband in order to distract their daughter Maya, whose name can be heard at the end of the original album track?

Lovin' You

Written with Richard Rudolf and produced with Stevie Wonder, the melody makes use of Riperton's extensive five-octave vocal range. The couple's daughter Maya Rudolph went on to find fame as an actress after appearing as a regular cast member on Saturday Night Live.

2 Which group recorded *Pick Up the Pieces* in 1974, which has no lyrics other than the occasional repetition of the song's title?

Average White Band

3 Delete one letter from each pair to reveal the name of Barry Manilow's first number-one single in the US:

BM RA NK ED YS

Mandy

4 On which 1972 album by Stevie Wonder do the tracks *Superstition* and *You Are the Sunshine of My Life* feature?

Talking Book

5 *I Am Woman* was a 1972 hit for which singer, whose debut album was titled *I Don't Know How to Love Him*?

Helen Reddy

6 Who wrote and recorded the 1974 hit *(You're) Having My Baby*, performed as a duet with Odia Coates?

Paul Anka

7 Which song by The O'Jays mentions the countries England, China, Egypt, and Israel in its lyrics?

Love Train

Rock Bands 3
QUESTIONS

1. Which rock band, whose name contains no vowels, released *Sweet Home Alabama* in 1974?

2. What is the title of the Queen album from which the singles *We Will Rock You* and *We Are the Champions* were released?

3. Which band released the album *London Calling* in 1979, with a title track that plays the Morse code for "SOS" in its closing section?

4. The name of which punk rock band, whose members all adopted the same surname, was inspired by a pseudonym used by Paul McCartney when checking into hotels?

5. Change one letter in each word below to reveal the name of the Fleetwood Mac song which was released as the US B-side to *Don't Stop*:

   FEVER DOING BUCK AGRIN

6. Irish singer and guitarist Phil Lynott was the frontman of which hard rock band, most famous for their 1976 single, *The Boys Are Back in Town*?

7. Sharing its name with a dinosaur, which British band released *Get It On*, *Children of the Revolution*, and *Telegram Sam* in the 1970s?

Rock Bands 3
ANSWERS

1 Which rock band, whose name contains no vowels, released *Sweet Home Alabama* in 1974?

Lynyrd Skynyrd

The band were originally known as My Backyard, but later changed their name to resemble that of a former schoolteacher named Leonard Skinner, who had criticized the boys' long hair. The politically charged lyrics of Sweet Home Alabama *are reportedly a response to lyrics in a song by Neil Young, whose name is prominently featured in the 1974 track.*

2 What is the title of the Queen album from which the singles *We Will Rock You* and *We Are the Champions* were released?

News of the World

3 Which band released the album *London Calling* in 1979, with a title track that plays the Morse code for "SOS" in its closing section?

The Clash

4 The name of which punk rock band, whose members all adopted the same surname, was inspired by a pseudonym used by Paul McCartney when checking into hotels?

The Ramones

5 Change one letter in each word below to reveal the name of the Fleetwood Mac song which was released as the US B-side to *Don't Stop*:

FEVER DOING BUCK AGRIN

Never Going Back Again

6 Irish singer and guitarist Phil Lynott was the frontman of which hard rock band, most famous for their 1976 single, *The Boys Are Back in Town*?

Thin Lizzy

7 Sharing its name with a dinosaur, which British band released *Get It On, Children of the Revolution*, and *Telegram Sam* in the 1970s?

T. Rex

Disco 3
QUESTIONS

1 Which song, previously recorded as a duet by Marvin Gaye and Tammi Terrell, became Diana Ross's first ever solo number one on the Billboard Hot 100, in 1970?

2 Which Manhattan suburb inspired the name of the band who released the 1978 hit, *Y.M.C.A.*?

3 Which Russian historical figure, who befriended Tsar Nicholas II, was the focus of a 1978 single by Boney M.?

4 What is the title of the Diana Ross song, recorded in 1979, which was co-written by Nile Rogers, who said he was inspired by drag performers impersonating the singer?

5 Which singer released *Got to Be Real* as a single from her self-titled debut album in 1978, which much later first charted in the UK in 2010?

6 Which Bee Gees song opens with the lyric, "Well you can tell by the way that I use my walk / I'm a woman's man, no time to talk"?

7 Restore the title of a 1976 single by The Trammps, from which all of the vowels have been removed and then the spacing changed:

D SCN FR N

1 Which song, previously recorded as a duet by Marvin Gaye and Tammi Terrell, became Diana Ross's first ever solo number one on the Billboard Hot 100, in 1970?

Ain't No Mountain High Enough

> *Previously frontwoman of The Supremes, Diana Ross released her version of the song as the second single from her eponymous debut solo album. Unlike the original, it features spoken-word passages performed by Ross, which were initially unpopular with Motown's Berry Gordy.*

2 Which Manhattan suburb inspired the name of the band who released the 1978 hit, *Y.M.C.A.?*

Greenwich Village

3 Which Russian historical figure, who befriended Tsar Nicholas II, was the focus of a 1978 single by Boney M.?

Grigori Rasputin

4 What is the title of the Diana Ross song, recorded in 1979, which was co-written by Nile Rogers, who said he was inspired by drag performers impersonating the singer?

I'm Coming Out

5 Which singer released *Got to Be Real* as a single from her self-titled debut album in 1978, which much later first charted in the UK in 2010?

Cheryl Lynn

6 Which Bee Gees song opens with the lyric, "Well you can tell by the way that I use my walk / I'm a woman's man, no time to talk"?

Stayin' Alive

7 Restore the title of a 1976 single by The Trammps, from which all of the vowels have been removed and then the spacing changed:

D SCN FR N

Disco Inferno

Singer-Songwriters 3
QUESTIONS

1 What is the title of the Carole King track that was released alongside *It's Too Late* in 1971, effectively forming a double A-side?

2 On which 1971 album, produced and written entirely by Joni Mitchell, can the song *A Case of You* be found?

3 Which 1973 song, written by Bob Marley, contains the lyrics "All around my home town / They're trying to track me down"?

4 Which song, originally released by Marvin Gaye, was covered by James Taylor on his album *Gorilla*?

5 What is the name of the musical group who have been Bruce Springsteen's primary backing band since 1972?

6 In which 1971 song does Bill Withers sing the phrase "I know" 26 times in succession, a refrain which was originally used as a gap-filler during composition but then was kept for the final recording?

7 Rearrange the letters below to reveal the title of a 1973 song by Carly Simon:

TIGHTEN HOT HOT GRID
(3, 5, 5, 2, 2)

Singer-Songwriters 3

ANSWERS

1 What is the title of the Carole King track that was released alongside *It's Too Late* in 1971, effectively forming a double A-side?

I Feel the Earth Move

> *The song, which prominently features King's piano-playing, went to number one on the Billboard Hot 100, remaining there for five consecutive weeks. Unusually, both of the tracks on the single made the Billboard top spot individually, which was at the time gradually becoming seen as the "official" singles chart of the United States.*

2 On which 1971 album, produced and written entirely by Joni Mitchell, can the song *A Case of You* be found?

Blue

3 Which 1973 song, written by Bob Marley, contains the lyrics "All around my home town / They're trying to track me down"?

I Shot the Sheriff

4 Which song, originally released by Marvin Gaye, was covered by James Taylor on his album *Gorilla*?

How Sweet It Is (To Be Loved by You)

5 What is the name of the musical group who have been Bruce Springsteen's primary backing band since 1972?

E Street Band

6 In which 1971 song does Bill Withers sing the phrase "I know" 26 times in succession, a refrain which was originally used as a gap-filler during composition but then was kept for the final recording?

Ain't No Sunshine

7 Rearrange the letters below to reveal the title of a 1973 song by Carly Simon:

TIGHTEN HOT HOT GRID
(3, 5, 5, 2, 2)

The Right Thing to Do

Legends 3
QUESTIONS

1 What name was Elton Hercules John given at birth, before he later legally changed his name in 1972?

2 Which Blondie album features cover art showing the band dressed in black and white, against a striped background, and an unsmiling Debbie Harry?

3 Which band—whose name was created from the surnames of two of its members—released a self-titled album in 1975, featuring the track *Rhiannon*?

4 Which song by The Jackson 5, with an extremely short title, knocked The Beatles's *Let It Be* off the top of the Billboard Hot 100 in 1970?

5 With which British novelist does Kate Bush share a birthday, whose only novel inspired one of her best-known hits?

6 Rearrange the letters below to reveal the title of a 1977 album from Billy Joel:

STRENGTH EAR (3, 8)

7 Which singer released *The Way We Were* in 1973, to coincide with the film of the same name in which she starred?

Legends 3
ANSWERS

1 What name was Elton Hercules John given at birth, before he later legally changed his name in 1972?

Reginald Kenneth Dwight

The man now known as Elton John created his own moniker from the names of two other musicians: Elton Dean and Long John Baldry. The singer is also sometimes affectionately referred to as the "Rocket Man", after his hit single of the same name—a nickname which was later used as the title of a 2019 biographical film.

2 Which Blondie album features cover art showing the band dressed in black and white, against a striped background, and an unsmiling Debbie Harry?

Parallel Lines

3 Which band—whose name was created from the surnames of two of its members—released a self-titled album in 1975, featuring the track *Rhiannon*?

Fleetwood Mac

4 Which song by The Jackson 5, with an extremely short title, knocked The Beatles's *Let It Be* off the top of the Billboard Hot 100 in 1970?

ABC

5 With which British novelist does Kate Bush share a birthday, whose only novel inspired one of her best-known hits?

Emily Brontë

6 Rearrange the letters below to reveal the title of a 1977 album from Billy Joel:

STRENGTH EAR (3, 8)

The Stranger

7 Which singer released *The Way We Were* in 1973, to coincide with the film of the same name in which she starred?

Barbra Streisand

Music at the Movies
QUESTIONS

1 On which film soundtrack can the tracks *Cantina Band* and *Rescue of the Princess* be found?

2 Change one letter in each word below to reveal the name of the Bill Conti song which serves as the theme tune for the 1976 film, *Rocky*:

DONNA FLU NEW

3 Which of these songs does *not* feature on the soundtrack to the 1977 film, *Saturday Night Fever*?

a. *Stayin' Alive*
b. *How Can You Mend a Broken Heart*
c. *More Than a Woman*
d. *Jive Talkin'*

4 Which former member of the Four Seasons sang the title track for *Grease*, written by Barry Gibb of the Bee Gees?

5 Which 1976 musical film features the songs *Fat Sam's Grand Slam*, *So You Wanna Be a Boxer?*, and *My Name is Tallulah*?

6 Which solo artist performed the theme song for the 1974 James Bond film, *The Man with the Golden Gun*?

7 During which 1972 film does the instrumental track *The Halls of Fear* feature, composed by Nino Rota?

Music at the Movies

ANSWERS

1 On which film soundtrack can the tracks *Cantina Band* and *Rescue of the Princess* be found?

Star Wars

Written for the first Star Wars *film, which would later be retroactively subtitled* Episode IV—A New Hope, *the soundtrack was composed by John Williams, winning him the Academy Award for Best Original Score for his work. A disco version of the film's main theme was a hit for Meco in 1977.*

2 Change one letter in each word below to reveal the name of the Bill Conti song which serves as the theme tune for the 1976 film, *Rocky*:

DONNA FLU NEW

Gonna Fly Now

3 Which of these songs does *not* feature on the soundtrack to the 1977 film, *Saturday Night Fever*?

a. *Stayin' Alive*
b. *How Can You Mend a Broken Heart*
c. *More Than a Woman*
d. *Jive Talkin'*

b. How Can You Mend a Broken Heart

4 Which former member of the Four Seasons sang the title track for *Grease*, written by Barry Gibb of the Bee Gees?

Frankie Valli

5 Which 1976 musical film features the songs *Fat Sam's Grand Slam*, *So You Wanna Be a Boxer?*, and *My Name is Tallulah*?

Bugsy Malone

6 Which solo artist performed the theme song for the 1974 James Bond film, *The Man with the Golden Gun*?

Lulu

7 During which 1972 film does the instrumental track *The Halls of Fear* feature, composed by Nino Rota?

The Godfather

One-Hit Wonders 2
QUESTIONS

1. Which song, covered by Debby Boone in 1977, set a record for most consecutive weeks at the top of the Billboard Top 100, staying in that position for ten weeks in total?

2. Delete one letter from each pair below to reveal the name of a song by Pilot, inspired by an Edinburgh sunrise:

   WM HA OG IA SC

3. Who released *Ring My Bell* in 1979, which went to number one in both the US and the UK?

4. What song by The Hues Corporation spawned a dance craze, particularly popular in Ireland, which involves participants sitting down and pretending to row?

5. *How Long* was a hit for which British band, whose bass player inspired the lyrics after being found to be secretly performing with other musicians?

6. Which band, with a name inspired by a character from the book that was adapted into the musical *Cats*, released *In the Summertime* in 1970?

7. Which song by Harry Chapin begins with the line, "My child arrived just the other day", with lyrics describing a father-son relationship?

One-Hit Wonders 2

ANSWERS

1 Which song, covered by Debby Boone in 1977, set a record for most consecutive weeks at the top of the Billboard Top 100, staying in that position for ten weeks in total?

You Light Up My Life

> *The original recording of the song by Kasey Cisyk has also been hugely successful, winning both an Academy Award and a Golden Globe for Best Original Song for a film of the same name. Boone's version became the best-selling single of the 1970s, although its ten-week stretch at number one was later matched by Olivia Newton John's Physical.*

2 Delete one letter from each pair below to reveal the name of a song by Pilot, inspired by an Edinburgh sunrise:

WM HA OG IA SC

Magic

3 Who released *Ring My Bell* in 1979, which went to number one in both the US and the UK?

Anita Ward

4 What song by The Hues Corporation spawned a dance craze, particularly popular in Ireland, which involves participants sitting down and pretending to row?

Rock the Boat

5 *How Long* was a hit for which British band, whose bass player inspired the lyrics after being found to be secretly performing with other musicians?

Ace

6 Which band, with a name inspired by a character from the book that was adapted into the musical *Cats*, released *In the Summertime* in 1970?

Mungo Jerry

7 Which song by Harry Chapin begins with the line, "My child arrived just the other day", with lyrics describing a father-son relationship?

Cat's in the Cradle

GAMES & TECH

The 70s was an era of huge technological leaps and when existing inventions, such as computers, became more compact and therefore more suited to the home. The first cell phone (commonly known as "the brick") hit the market, the first email was sent, and the digital video camera was first invented.

Synchronize your digital watch because it's time to invite over a few Space Invaders to embark on a Colossal (Cave) Adventure as you serve up the answers just like a game of Pong. Make it through this round, and she'll be Apple(s)!

Pong
QUESTIONS

1. Which sport, which has been part of the summer Olympics since 1988, inspired the name of the 1972 arcade game, *Pong*?

2. What feature of *Pong* is designed to limit the length of a game by making it get progressively harder?

3. How many items appear on screen at once during a game of *Pong*?

4. How many points does a player need to reach to beat their opponent, in an original arcade game of *Pong*?

5. What mechanical fault caused the first ever *Pong* arcade machine to stop working properly, a few days after installation?

6. Restore the missing vowels, and change the spacing, to reveal the founding father of the video games industry, and co-founder of Atari, who commissioned Allan Alcorn to create *Pong*:

   NL NBS HN LL

7. One of the release titles for the Atari 2600 console included *Pong* as well as several variants. What was its title?

ANSWERS

1 Which sport, which has been part of the summer Olympics since 1988, inspired the name of the 1972 arcade game, *Pong*?

Table tennis

> *The name* Pong *comes from the second word of table tennis's alternative name, ping pong. The game itself, however, was inspired by an existing console property, which was in turn said to have been inspired by the game of tennis.*

2 What feature of *Pong* is designed to limit the length of a game by making it get progressively harder?

The ball speeds up over time

3 How many items appear on screen at once during a game of *Pong*?

Six: two scores, two paddles, a ball and a net

4 How many points does a player need to reach to beat their opponent, in an original arcade game of *Pong*?

11

5 What mechanical fault caused the first ever *Pong* arcade machine to stop working properly, a few days after installation?

The coin mechanism was jammed with too many coins having been inserted

6 Restore the missing vowels, and change the spacing, to reveal the founding father of the video games industry, and co-founder of Atari, who commissioned Allan Alcorn to create *Pong*:

NL NBS HN LL

Nolan Bushnell

7 One of the release titles for the Atari 2600 console included *Pong* as well as several variants. What was its title?

Video Olympics

Home Consoles 1

1 What was the name of the machine, released by Magnavox in 1972, that is now recognized as the first commercial home video game console?

2 Which 1977 console from Atari was supplied with two joystick controllers and a joined pair of paddle controllers?

3 What did the "F" stand for in the name of the Fairchild Channel F?

4 The Color TV-Game was the first ever video game system from which company that went on to create several iconic gaming brands, as well as a series of future consoles?

5 Coleco used what brand name for their series of video game consoles released from 1976 to 1978, sharing its name with early communication satellites?

6 Midway, part of Bally, created the 1978 console that was later renamed to the Astrocade, but what name was used on its original 1978 release?

7 Which well-known US toy manufacturer released the Intellivision console in 1979, considered the world's first 16-bit games console?

Home Consoles 1

1 What was the name of the machine, released by Magnavox in 1972, that is now recognized as the first commercial home video game console?

Magnavox Odyssey

The machine came with two rectangular controllers, connected to a TV for its output, and could run on six C batteries if desired. It came with overlay sheets that you could stick onto your television in order to make content look more visually interesting, since its games were only capable of displaying three square dots and a vertical line.

2 Which 1977 console from Atari was supplied with two joystick controllers and a joined pair of paddle controllers?

Atari 2600 / Atari VCS / Atari Video Computer System

3 What did the "F" stand for in the name of the Fairchild Channel F?

Fun

4 The Color TV-Game was the first ever video game system from which company that went on to create several iconic gaming brands, as well as a series of future consoles?

Nintendo

5 Coleco used what brand name for their series of video game consoles released from 1976 to 1978, sharing its name with early communication satellites?

Telstar

6 Midway, part of Bally, created the 1978 console that was later renamed to the Astrocade, but what name was used on its original 1978 release?

Bally Professional Arcade— although it was marketed in 1977 as the Bally Home Library Computer

7 Which well-known US toy manufacturer released the Intellivision console in 1979, considered the world's first 16-bit games console?

Mattel

Asteroids
QUESTIONS

1. When you first hit an asteroid in the 1979 Atari arcade game, *Asteroids*, how many fragments does it split into?

2. What happened if you went off the edges of the screen during a game of *Asteroids*?

3. What other obstacles could appear on screen, which would shoot bullets at the player?

4. Which size of asteroid moved the fastest around the screen?
   a. The largest ones
   b. The medium-sized ones
   c. The smallest ones
   d. They all moved at the same speed

5. Unjumble the following letters to reveal the name of the feature that, if used, provided an instantaneous one-in-six chance of sudden death:

   PRAY SPEECH (10)

6. What was special about the display technology used for the game, certainly compared to any modern arcade game?

7. Highly accomplished *Asteroids* players generally find that the game slows down as they continue to play for long periods of time. Why is this?

1 When you first hit an asteroid in the 1979 Atari arcade game, *Asteroids*, how many fragments does it split into?

Two

The game starts off with four large asteroids on screen, but when hit each asteroid splits into two medium-sized asteroids. Each of these in turn splits into two more when hit, which then vanish when shot. Once the screen is clear, more large asteroids appear, and so the game continues forever.

2 What happened if you went off the edges of the screen during a game of *Asteroids*?

You came back on the other side

3 What other obstacles could appear on screen, which would shoot bullets at the player?

Flying saucers, of two different sizes

4 Which size of asteroid moved the fastest around the screen?

a. The largest ones
b. The medium-sized ones
c. The smallest ones
d. They all moved at the same speed

c. The smallest ones

5 Unjumble the following letters to reveal the name of the feature that, if used, provided an instantaneous one-in-six chance of sudden death:

PRAY SPEECH (10)

Hyperspace

6 What was special about the display technology used for the game, certainly compared to any modern arcade game?

It was a vector display, rather than bitmap-based, so there was no "pixelation"

7 Highly accomplished *Asteroids* players generally find that the game slows down as they continue to play for long periods of time. Why is this?

They continue to receive extra lives, so the game must continually redisplay more and more life symbols on screen— which slows the system down

Home Computers 1

1 What was the name of the MITS machine, released in January 1975, that kicked off the home computer revolution after appearing on the cover of *Popular Electronics* magazine?

2 Rearrange the letters below to reveal the name of the person who co-founded Microsoft in 1975, alongside Bill Gates:

A NULL LEAP (4, 5)

3 In 1978, Rockwell released a redesigned and expanded version of the MOS KIM-1, with what name ending in a two-digit number?

4 Despite the number in the name of the Commodore PET 2001, what year of the 1970s was it actually launched in?

5 What superlative name was given to Intertec's 1979 machine, featuring a curved all-in-one injection-molded case?

6 Which US-wide chain store launched the TRS-80 in 1977, a computer that came with everything required to run it and with no assembly required?

7 Which famous electronics engineer, known affectionately by the nickname "Woz", designed the Apple I, known at the time as the Apple Computer 1?

Home Computers 1

1 What was the name of the MITS machine, released in January 1975, that kicked off the home computer revolution after appearing on the cover of *Popular Electronics* magazine?

Altair 8800

The image featured on the cover of the magazine was not actually of the real computer, since the first machine made, sent off to the magazine, had been lost following a courier strike, and there wasn't time to make another before it went to press. Nonetheless the company were soon inundated with orders.

2 Rearrange the letters below to reveal the name of the person who co-founded Microsoft in 1975, alongside Bill Gates:

A NULL LEAP (4, 5)

Paul Allen

3 In 1978, Rockwell released a redesigned and expanded version of the MOS KIM-1, with what name ending in a two-digit number?

AIM-65

4 Despite the number in the name of the Commodore PET 2001, what year of the 1970s was it actually launched in?

1977

5 What superlative name was given to Intertec's 1979 machine, featuring a curved all-in-one injection-molded case?

Superbrain

6 Which US-wide chain store launched the TRS-80 in 1977, a computer that came with everything required to run it and with no assembly required?

Radio Shack—and by Tandy in the UK

7 Which famous electronics engineer, known affectionately by the nickname "Woz", designed the Apple I, known at the time as the Apple Computer 1?

Steve Wozniak

Pioneers
QUESTIONS

1 Unjumble the following letters to reveal the name of the founder of Commodore, creator of the hugely successful PET computer:

MERIT JACKAL (4, 7)

2 Ted Dabney co-founded which hugely significant video game and home computer company?

3 Microsoft sold their first-ever product, a version of the BASIC programming language, for use on which 1975 computer?

4 Federico Faggin helped design which Intel architecture in 1972, a follow up to the existing 8008 design and which later influenced the hugely successful 8086?

5 Delete one letter from each pair below to reveal the name of a computer programming language designed by pioneer Niklaus Wirth:

CP AL SE VC AO LD

6 After joining MOS Technology, Charles "Chuck" Peddle was the designer of which influential and successful microprocessor family?

7 Clive Sinclair created which hugely successful electronic product in 1972, selling over 100,000 a month at the peak of its success?

ANSWERS

1 Unjumble the following letters to reveal the name of the founder of Commodore, creator of the hugely successful PET computer:

MERIT JACKAL (4, 7)

Jack Tramiel

> *Tramiel's impressive legacy encompasses not only the PET but also the VIC-20 and Commodore 64. His machines were so successful that he famously placed a 1983 advert, at the height of Commodore's success, boldly stating "Commodore Ate the Apple". He later went on to form Atari Corporation from the remains of the original Atari Inc, overseeing the creation of the Atari ST, Lynx, and Jaguar.*

2 Ted Dabney co-founded which hugely significant video game and home computer company?

Atari

3 Microsoft sold their first-ever product, a version of the BASIC programming language, for use on which 1975 computer?

MITS Altair 8800

4 Federico Faggin helped design which Intel architecture in 1972, a follow up to the existing 8008 design and which later influenced the hugely successful 8086?

Intel 8080

5 Delete one letter from each pair below to reveal the name of a computer programming language designed by pioneer Niklaus Wirth:

CP AL SE VC AO LD

Pascal

6 After joining MOS Technology, Charles "Chuck" Peddle was the designer of which influential and successful microprocessor family?

The 650x family of processors —of which the 6502 was the most successful

7 Clive Sinclair created which hugely successful electronic product in 1972, selling over 100,000 a month at the peak of its success?

A pocket calculator, the Sinclair Executive

Space Invaders
QUESTIONS

1. Game developer Tomohiro Nishikado created *Space Invaders* for which Japanese arcade manufacturer?

2. How many rows of aliens appear on the first screen of a *Space Invaders* game?

3. In what year was *Space Invaders* first released?

4. A *Space Invaders* player can hide behind stationary defense bunkers at the bottom of the screen. How many of these are present at the start of the game?

5. In the original arcade releases, what two colors of cellophane were added to the screen to make the black-and-white graphics more colorful?

6. What changes about *Space Invader*'s gameplay as you start to destroy more and more aliens, adding more pressure to clear the level?

7. What famous Atari arcade game does Tomohiro Nishikado cite as having been the original inspiration for the game?

Space Invaders
ANSWERS

1 Game developer Tomohiro Nishikado created *Space Invaders* for which Japanese arcade manufacturer?

Taito

Taito was founded in 1953 and started to sell arcade games from 1974 onward. For Space Invaders's *overseas sales, however, they sold the rights to Midway, a division of Bally, and it became Midway's first mainstream hit in the United States.*

2 How many rows of aliens appear on the first screen of a *Space Invaders* game?

5 rows—each with 11 aliens

3 In what year was *Space Invaders* first released?

1978

4 A *Space Invaders* player can hide behind stationary defense bunkers at the bottom of the screen. How many of these are present at the start of the game?

4 bunkers

5 In the original arcade releases, what two colors of cellophane were added to the screen to make the black-and-white graphics more colorful?

Green and orange

6 What changes about *Space Invader's* gameplay as you start to destroy more and more aliens, adding more pressure to clear the level?

They begin to move faster and faster towards the player

7 What famous Atari arcade game does Tomohiro Nishikado cite as having been the original inspiration for the game?

Breakout

Home Computers 2
QUESTIONS

1 Atari released two home computers in 1979, both essentially significantly updated versions of the preceding Atari VCS console. Which of these two computers was notable for its membrane keyboard?

2 Why did the Apple logo used on the Apple II computer feature a rainbow of colors running across the image?

3 Which large US company released the TI 99/4 in 1979, notable for being the first 16-bit home computer?

4 What is the meaning of the word "chiclet" when used in association with the Commodore PET computer?

5 What was the target environment for Research Machines's 1978 highly expandable computer, the 380Z?

6 Replace the missing vowels, and change the spacing, to reveal the name of computing pioneer Clive Sinclair's company that released the MK 14, their first home computer, in 1978:

S CN CFC MBR DG

7 The System 1 was an exposed-circuitboard computer with a 25-button keypad, created by which UK computer manufacturer that would later go on to design the BBC Micro?

Home Computers 2
ANSWERS

1 Atari released two home computers in 1979, both essentially significantly updated versions of the preceding Atari VCS console. Which of these two computers was notable for its membrane keyboard?

Atari 400

> *The other machine was the Atari 800, which had both a full-travel keyboard and more RAM, as well as greater expandability. Internally, however, Atari referred to the two models using the names of in-house secretaries, Candy and Colleen, with Candy being marketed as a games machine and Colleen as a more serious computer.*

2 Why did the Apple logo used on the Apple II computer feature a rainbow of colors running across the image?

The machine could display multiple colors, unlike many competing systems

3 Which large US company released the TI 99/4 in 1979, notable for being the first 16-bit home computer?

Texas Instruments

4 What is the meaning of the word "chiclet" when used in association with the Commodore PET computer?

It refers to the square-keyed, limited-travel keyboard

5 What was the target environment for Research Machines's 1978 highly expandable computer, the 380Z?

Classrooms / education

6 Replace the missing vowels, and change the spacing, to reveal the name of computing pioneer Clive Sinclair's company that released the MK 14, their first home computer, in 1978:

S CN CFC MBR DG

Science of Cambridge

7 The System 1 was an exposed-circuitboard computer with a 25-button keypad, created by which UK computer manufacturer that would later go on to design the BBC Micro?

Acorn Computers

Technology

1 What was the name of the C-shaped machine, first installed at Los Alamos National Laboratory in 1976, that went on to become synonymous with the word "supercomputer" for decades?

2 The Xerox Alto was famous for being the first personal computer to use what type of interface, later acknowledged to have been hugely influential on Steve Jobs in creating the Apple Lisa and Macintosh?

3 Which videocassette format had gained 60% of the North American market by the end of the 1970s, becoming the dominant video format for the next decade or more?

4 In what year of the 1970s did Hamilton introduce the world's first digital wristwatch?

5 Released in 1978, what was the name of the first commercially available optical video disc system, a precursor to later DVD, and Blu-ray discs?

6 What type of device was the IBM Selectric II, introduced to offices—and some homes—in 1971?

7 Betamax, a format which fought for dominance throughout the second half of the 1970s, was what type of system?

1 What was the name of the C-shaped machine, first installed at Los Alamos National Laboratory in 1976, that went on to become synonymous with the word "supercomputer" for decades?

Cray-1

> *The Cray-1 hugely improved performance over existing systems, consisting of tightly repeated circuitboards, arranged in stacks in the shape of a "C". The entire system was submerged in a coolant, to avoid overheating problems. In some installations the coolant would be dramatically lit and pumped over a "waterfall".*

2 The Xerox Alto was famous for being the first personal computer to use what type of interface, later acknowledged to have been hugely influential on Steve Jobs in creating the Apple Lisa and Macintosh?

Graphical user interface / desktop

In what year of the 1970s did Hamilton introduce the world's first digital wristwatch?

1972

6 What type of device was the IBM Selectric II, introduced to offices—and some homes—in 1971?

Electric typewriter

3 Which videocassette format had gained 60% of the North American market by the end of the 1970s, becoming the dominant video format for the next decade or more?

VHS—short for Video Home System

5 Released in 1978, what was the name of the first commercially available optical video disc system, a precursor to later DVD, and Blu-ray discs?

LaserDisc

7 Betamax, a format which fought for dominance throughout the second half of the 1970s, was what type of system?

A videocassette tape format

Home Consoles 2
QUESTIONS

1 Which board game manufacturer, that later became a division of Hasbro, was responsible for the 1979 console, the Microvision?

2 What add-on peripheral was required to play the Magnavox Odyssey games *Prehistoric Safari*, *Dogfight!*, and *Shootout!*?

3 Fill in the missing word to complete the name of the 1975 Atari console dedicated to playing a home version of an existing Atari arcade game:

Home _____

4 What was notable about the Fairchild Channel F upon its original release, in terms of the way its games could be chosen?

5 What was the name of the Atari console that featured motorcycle handlebars, inspired by the popularity of Evel Knievel?

6 What was the video resolution of the Atari 2600 (VCS) console, in terms of the number of pixels that could be displayed horizontally and vertically?

a. 160 × 192 pixels
b. 200 × 240 pixels
c. 240 × 288 pixels
d. 320 × 384 pixels

7 The pack-in games cartridge supplied with the Atari 2600 (VCS) was later changed to *Pac-Man*, but what game was originally supplied throughout the 1970s?

70s GAMES & TECH

1 Which board game manufacturer, that later became a division of Hasbro, was responsible for the 1979 console, the Microvision?

MB / Milton Bradley

> The Microvision is renowned for being the world's first handheld game console, due to its support for cartridges which allowed a range of games to be played. Unfortunately it had an extremely small screen and was not widely supported by games writers, so it was soon discontinued.

2 What add-on peripheral was required to play the Magnavox Odyssey games *Prehistoric Safari*, *Dogfight!*, and *Shootout!*?

A light gun, known as the Shooting Gallery

3 Fill in the missing word to complete the name of the 1975 Atari console dedicated to playing a home version of an existing Atari arcade game:

Home ____

Home Pong

4 What was notable about the Fairchild Channel F upon its original release, in terms of the way its games could be chosen?

It was the first cartridge-based console

5 What was the name of the Atari console that featured motorcycle handlebars, inspired by the popularity of Evel Knievel?

Atari Stunt Cycle

6 What was the video resolution of the Atari 2600 (VCS) console, in terms of the number of pixels that could be displayed horizontally and vertically?

a. 160 × 192 pixels
b. 200 × 240 pixels
c. 240 × 288 pixels
d. 320 × 384 pixels

a. 160 × 192 pixels

7 The pack-in games cartridge supplied with the Atari 2600 (VCS) was later changed to *Pac-Man*, but what game was originally supplied throughout the 1970s?

Combat

Electronic Toys

1 What is the name of the short-term memory game, featuring brightly colored red, yellow, green, and blue buttons, that was first released by Milton Bradley (MB) in 1978?

2 Texas Instruments released what iconic educational toy, known for its audio pronunciations of various words, which came in a robust red plastic case with built-in keyboard?

3 Invicta Plastics released an electronic version of which code-breaking board game in 1977, replacing the colored pegs of the original version with digital numbers?

4 Which 1978 Parker Brothers handheld electronic game, looks visually like an early telephone handset and allows the player to choose from six built-in games?

5 Mattel released a series of digital games under the Mattel Electronics brand. What was the name of the first of these, featuring a stylized top-down image of a Formula One car?

6 In 1979 Milton Bradley (MB) released which six-wheeled, two-track electronic toy vehicle, which came with a keypad on its top surface that allowed you to program in sequences of moves?

7 The Computer Perfection was a relatively simple electronic toy presented to look like a space-age circular console, leading to it being featured in which US TV sci-fi series?

Electronic Toys
ANSWERS

1 What is the name of the short-term memory game, featuring brightly colored red, yellow, green, and blue buttons, that was first released by Milton Bradley (MB) in 1978?

Simon

> *The device was so successful that it remains on sale today, and followed on from MB's first electronic game, the Logic 5. The bold, cheerful design of the Simon made it visually attractive both in toy stores and in use, and with four starting skill levels and an ever-increasing difficulty while in play it was able to provide a suitable challenge for all ages of player.*

2 Texas Instruments released what iconic educational toy, known for its audio pronunciations of various words, which came in a robust red plastic case with built-in keyboard?

Speak & Spell

3 Invicta Plastics released an electronic version of which code-breaking board game in 1977, replacing the colored pegs of the original version with digital numbers?

Master Mind

4 Which 1978 Parker Brothers handheld electronic game, looks visually like an early telephone handset and allows the player to choose from six built-in games?

Merlin / Merlin the Electronic Wizard

5 Mattel released a series of digital games under the Mattel Electronics brand. What was the name of the first of these, featuring a stylized top-down image of a Formula One car?

Mattel Auto Race

6 In 1979 Milton Bradley (MB) released which six-wheeled, two-track electronic toy vehicle, which came with a keypad on its top surface that allowed you to program in sequences of moves?

Big Trak

7 The Computer Perfection was a relatively simple electronic toy presented to look like a space-age circular console, leading to it being featured in which US TV sci-fi series?

Buck Rogers in the 25th Century